# Don't Ever Tell Me You Can't

## CELIA RUIZ-TOMLINSON

Virtualbookworm.com Publishing, Inc.
P.O. Box 9949, College Station,
TX 77842, U.S.A.

DE LA SALLE UNIVERSITY PRESS, INC.
2169 Fidel A. Reyes Street
Malate 1004, Manila, Philippines

First published in 2001 by
Virtualbookworm.com Publishing, Inc.
P. O. Box 9949, College Station
TX 77842, U.S.A.

Philippine edition published in 2005 by
DE LA SALLE UNIVERSITY PRESS, INC.
2169 Fidel A. Reyes Street
Malate 1004, Manila, Philippines
Tel. Nos.: (632) 536-1761 and 526-5139
Telefax: (632) 526-5052
E-mail: press@dlsu.edu.ph
Website: http://press.dlsu.edu.ph

---

**Cataloguing-in-Publication Data**

---

TA        Tomlinson, Celia Ruiz
140            Don't ever tell me you can't / by Celia Ruiz-Tomlinson.—Philippine
.T145      ed.—Manila: De La Salle University Press, 2005.
2005           x; 171 p.; cm

     First published: College Station, TX, U.S.A.: Virtualbookworm.com
Pub., 2001

     ISBN: 9-7155-5515-2

     1. Tomlinson, Celia Ruiz. 2. Civil Engineers—Philippines—
Biography. I. Title.

---

*Basal Text:* John Handy LET
*Display Type:* Esprit Book
*Typesetting System:* Adobe Pagemaker 7.0
*Paper Stock:* Bookpaper #60
*Cover Design:* Anthony S. Crisostomo

# Table of Contents

# Acknowledgments

The writing of this book had been a pure work of passion and conviction. I believed it is a great story of courage, determination, and resilience—a classic human success story. I believed I must write it in my own words because it is a case of the "singer and the song." I believed it must be published so it may benefit readers who are inclined to be inspired and motivated. I so believed in the project that I vowed to get it done if it took me 25 years.

It did take 25 years from the time the idea of writing the book hit me to the moment the first hardcover was handed to me. In that span of a quarter of a century, many individuals believed in the project, too, that it would be remiss of me if I did not acknowledge the help and encouragement that I received from them along the way.

My father was living with my family in Albuquerque when I started writing the book. He would bring me hot steaming coffee when he heard the clicking of the typewriter keys in the wee hours of the morning. Unfortunately, he never saw the final product. My mother did everything in our house, freeing me to pursue my passion and conviction.

My sister, Ruby, typed one of the first versions of the manuscript for free. She gave me words of encouragement, in spite of the uncomplimentary paragraphs written about her entry into my life.

My first and only literary agent, Joyce H. Wright of Creative Literary Services, in Virginia, took me on as a non-paying client because she honestly believed in the merit of my story. She edited the manuscript and heaven knows she tried like hell to sell it to major New York publishers.

Bonnie Jones Reynolds, herself an author *(Truth About Unicorns, The Confettiman,* and *Birkham's Beginning Yoga Class).* Bonnie and I found each other through an announcement that she had placed in *The*

*Writer*, a magazine for writers. She wanted to publish one or two books based on true stories about the triumph of the human spirit. I submitted my manuscript. It was one of the literally hundreds that she received in the mail from all over the United States. She selected my manuscript, and one other from another author, to be the first books to be published by her upstart Consider the Lilies Publications. Unfortunately, she ran into difficult times and her plans never materialized. Fortunately for me, she edited my manuscript and gave me suggestions that led to the final form of the book. For a while, she tried to place my book with another publisher.

Bobby Bernshausen, the owner of Virtualbookworm.com Publishing, Inc. of Texas, one of the first print-on-demand publishers in the market, accepted my manuscript for publication as an e-book without charge, because he believed in its merit.

My late husband, Tom, whom I bombarded with every little news of the ups and downs in my pursuit of publication all those 25 years, arranged the first booksigning when the hardcover finally came out.

Oscar Ongpin, a former classmate of mine at Mapua Institute of Technology, on his own, sent press releases about the book to the Filipino media in California.

Linda Nietes, whose unwavering belief in the Filipino author is the driving force behind the Philippine Expressions Bookshop, launched my book at the Philippine Consulate in Los Angeles, upon the offering of Consul General Ruth Morales Prado.

Ernie Delfin, columnist of the *Philippine Star*, tirelessly praised my book and even compared it with Carlos Bulosan's *America is in the Heart*. He bought a hundred copies and gave them to deserving readers.

The De La Salle University Press in Manila believes in printing the Philippine edition of the book, although it lies on the fringes of the scope of the academic press' mission. In particular, I thank Bro. Andrew Gonzalez, FSC, publisher; Edna Formilleza, director; Alejandro Padilla, editor; Franz Louise Santos, layout artist; and Anthony Crisostomo, cover designer.

Of course, I thank Jimmy Cura for writing the introduction for this edition.

There are many unnamed others who contributed in some form or another to the success of the book. To them I am very grateful.

# Foreword

I t has been a few years since this epic autobiography of Celia R. Tomlinson first saw print. Her story, however, remains as timely and engaging as when she first wrote it. It resonates among the millions of Filipinos—many of them women—who leave the Philippines daily in droves to seek new beginnings and better opportunities in foreign lands as a means to break out of the bondage of poverty and penury.

Tomlinson graphically narrates her family's transition from the placid rural environment of their provincial hometown to the rough-and-tumble, dog-eat-dog urban jungle of Metropolitan Manila. Her narration reads like a screenplay for a movie on the squatter problem of the metropolis. It evokes images of the teeming masses of urban migrants who leave their rural homes for the imagined comforts of the big city, only to find out that they have jumped from the proverbial frying pan into the fire.

It is against this backdrop that the story zooms in on Celia while bringing out the varying characters of the members of her family, particularly her parents, and their influence on her personal upbringing.

Celia's story is a living thesis on the role of values and principles for a successful life—in forging one's persona, in charting one's career, in making choices and being accountable for them, in learing from one's mistakes and using the hard-earned lessons to move on, in setting goals and pursuing them no matter what the cost, in having a steadfast faith in God and in one's self even in the face of adversity, in interacting with people and being able to pick out friend from foe, in learning to separate the chaff from the grain.

Ranged against the odds emanating from her humble beginnings,

# Foreword

Celia's achievements are by no means paltry. She completes a college education at one of the finest engineering schools in the Philippines. She passes the licensure examination and breaks into the exclusive circles of a male-dominated profession. Scrounging up just enough money for a plane ticket, she leaves her homeland to try her luck in the United States of America.

After an unbelievable struggle, she finally lands a job as a professional engineer, breaking down the walls of male chauvinism at work, marrying into a true-blue Caucasian American family, and, with her husband Tom, eventually setting up her own business which, even after the demise of Tom, she oversees and manages to this day.

The folksy title of Celia R. Tomlinson's book aptly summarizes her message to all her fellow Filipinos in particular, and to all kindred spirits in general: *We are limited only by the boundaries that we impose upon ourselves.*

In a very real sense, the sky is the limit. At this day and age when young people are short on real-life heroes, reading the book might just be what young people need.

— Jaime "Jimmy" A. Cura
Governor 2005-2006, Rotary International D-3830
Chairman, Progressive Times Action Group (PTAG-Phils.)

*Dedicated to the memory of my father, Felix Ruiz, whose idea it was that I become a civil engineer. Upon this idea, a dream beyond engineering was born.*

# Chapter 1

# The Difference

When the Pan American Airlines jet touched the pavement of Los Angeles International Airport in August 1968, I nearly burst with delight. I had been an established civil engineer from the Philippines for the past three years, and had worked as a land surveyor before that. Now I was overjoyed to walk on the soil of the United States of America where I had long dreamed of living. One of the optimistic technologists who responded to President Lyndon Johnson's announcement of a technical manpower shortage, I had come by myself, confident that $300 in pocket money and a civil engineer's diploma were enough to found a new life in the land of opportunity.

Two days later, however, when I set out to look for a job, I received shocking news: *"We hire only men,"* the Personnel Manager of an engineering company told me. His stare was fixed on my eyes. "You can't find a job as a civil engineer anywhere," his voice filled with sarcasm. Stunned, I broke down and sobbed. I remembered with dismay how my parents, brothers and sisters had smashed their coconut-shell banks to raise my pocket money. The thought of returning home a pathetic failure staggered me.

At first I went from one engineering firm to another searching for someone to tell me I had a chance. After two days, I stopped. I did not want to wear out my host's hospitality and I had to move on before my pocket money got depleted. But I vehemently refused to go back to the Philippines. I would not accept the Personnel Manager's warning that I would never make it in engineering in this county. I also ignored the advice of newfound acquaintances that suggested I work as a babysitter or cocktail waitress.

## Celia Ruiz-Tomlinson

I was poignantly conscious of the preciousness of my civil engineer's diploma. As a 16-year-old college freshman, I had seen three young women—my only female classmates—drop out of engineering school one by one because they could no longer endure the harassment directed at us by hostile professors. To get the practical knowledge needed to pass the board examinations, I had spent numerous hours near construction sites, looking in from the outside through chainlink fences because builders not only refused to hire women engineers, they wouldn't even allow them in the premises. "I did not work so hard and so long for my degree only to give it up!" I said and I set out to prove that I could earn the good life of a civil engineer in America.

When I became New Mexico's first female field engineer and inspector in 1977, 1 knew I had arrived—nearly a decade later. The project was a mere quarter of a million-dollar job; nevertheless, it was a breakthrough for women. It attracted the attention of the press. I remember as a Scripps-Howard newsman's camera clicked away, I smiled and smiled and smiled while I posed crawling in and out of a newly-built manhole. Talk about great moments! A heavy-duty crane couldn't have dragged me out of the scene. What I felt was an almost palpable sense of strength and a special joy—joy in my identity, joy in being a woman, joy in adversities overcome.

Now, I *own* an engineering company. I am the President and CEO of an engineering company that I founded in 1983. Founded with $2,000, rented surveying instruments, and a laborer hired out of the State of New Mexico's unemployment line, the company— Rhombus Professional Associates—has grown into a full-service engineering company that employs engineers, surveyors, and environmental scientists. Pardon me for sounding too triumphant, but an engineering company that is over 15 years old, founded and owned by a female engineer is still as rare as a clean manhole in a sewer system anywhere.

This is not just about engineering, entrepreneurship, feminism, or racism. This is about having a dream and pursuing it passionately. This is about tenacity, resilience, and triumph of the human spirit.

What goes into the making of a tenacious and resilient human being?

# Chapter 2

# The Roots

Friends often ask what possessed me to get into civil engineering, and I am always tempted to say that I had a touch of genius and a psychic vision that in the future engineering was the profession to be in. But I can't claim that. I took up engineering because my father made me do it.

When I was nearly five years old, Father always sent me off to attend the second-grade class of my older sister, Pag-asa. Attendance of younger siblings was usually allowed in this nipa school hut in San Miguel, Bulacan, a sleepy, balmy town in the central plains of Luzon, the Philippines. Its furnishings consisted of two wooden benches on packed dirt floor and a blackboard hanging by a rope on the wall.

I remember the teacher vividly. A lanky charcoal-haired woman whose skin was like satin, she always smelled of baby powder. Her shoulder-length wavy hair was parted in the middle and held behind her ears by bobby pins. When she told the pupils to read, I, too read for I already knew how. When she asked a question, I raised my hand higher than anyone else's to volunteer the answer. Such was my idea of fun—keeping up the pace with the second-graders and looking at them with pleasurable disdain. I was far ahead of them in learning.

How much behind I was I did not realize until the day the teacher instructed the class to draw an apple. I worked on the task enthusiastically but because my motor skills had not fully developed, I could not soften the curves of the drawing no matter how I tried. After numerous repeated attempts, the rubber eraser savagely punctured the lead-smudged paper. In frustration, I looked around to see if I was not alone in the predicament. To my dismay, I saw the other pupils doing just fine; their drawings did look like apples! I was speechless with envy. When the teacher approached to look at my work, self-pity washed over me, sending wild hot tears down my cheeks. "I can't draw an apple!" I blurted out. "I don't want school anymore!"

Before her comforting words could touch the depths of my self-indulgence, I ran out of the classroom, crying loud enough for the town's small population to know about the inequity within the school system. My bare feet treading the dusty road, I bawled past grassland interrupted only occasionally by nipa huts and grazing carabaos. I wailed past the town barber's front yard where men congregated to discuss the town's affairs.

"Who could that kid be shrieking like a boar being castrated?" the barber asked. He paused from cutting a man's hair, and craned his neck.

"It looks like your Celia, Felix," said another man who rose from the wooden bench and recognized me.

Confirming it was indeed I, Father leaped off the same bench and scurried to pick me up. As he held me in his arms, he frantically inspected my hands, legs, and head. "What happened? Where do you hurt?" He raised my smock to look at my back.

I continued my anguished cries. "I can't draw an apple. I'll never go back to school again." I arched backward, threw my head back and flung my arms in a tantrum.

Realizing that my tears were not for pain caused by a bleeding wound or a cracked bone, Father sighed with relief. He gently pushed my head on his shoulder, his shirt muffling my sobs, and patted me lovingly on the back. "But you should never give up school. School makes something good out of people."

Father had had the faith that school made something good out of people long before he became my father. When he was four years old, his father, a farmer, died of pneumonia. His mother, who had not known how to make a living, remarried and left him, along with his only brother, to the care of an uncle who taught him how to plow the rice field. But he enjoyed school more than farming, and he excelled as a student. He always brought home test papers marked with "Very Good." The schoolteachers picked him to tutor students who were weak in math. He went all over the province to participate in academic contests. In fact, he loved to tell me of fierce mathematics competitions between him and Luis Taruc, his classmate who later became the "supremo" of the *Hukbalahap*, a group of political dissidents of the late '40s. Only Taruc could come close to my caliber, he mentioned, repeatedly. Since Taruc was a real person, Father's stories became truly remarkable to me. They made me feel in touch with the historic past.

4

One day when he was sixteen years old, Felix committed a sin for which his guardian would punish him for life. On his way to register as a high school freshman, he rolled the dice, gambled with, and lost his tuition fee money. That ended his formal schooling, abruptly. Even when a schoolteacher who saw Felix's potentials offered to pay for his education, his uncle categorically refused. "Hell, no. He had his chance," he boomed. "He blew it once and for all."

Felix sought his mother's help, but she, too, could not be convinced. Being totally dependent on her new husband's livelihood, she wielded no influence on their budget. The educational deprivation stuck in Felix's mind and his life was never the same again. Every time schools opened for the season, his heart pounded heavily and a gnawing pain in the pit of his stomach sharpened. He thought the devil was ridiculing him, reminding him that he would never set foot again in the school he had enjoyed so much. After a few years and with nothing else to look forward to, he married Anacleta, a precocious girl from the same town.

Anacleta's earliest memory was of being taken away by her mother for a brisk walk. Her parents often quarreled and this was one of the times they were parting.

"Anacleta and I are moving out of this house," her mother declared unequivocally. "I can support ourselves. I don't have to put up with you." With that, she and her mother headed out, leaving her father astounded.

Anacleta was only four then and she remembered walking barefoot, holding on to her mother's hand, through a grassy path between bamboo groves, then along a riverbank. Carrying a tin wash basin filled with bare needs like clothes, salt, rice, and a gas lamp, her mother was searching for a vacant hut they could move into and spend the rest of their lives.

Anacleta had no idea what her parents fought about, but it did not seem to matter because her fate was already sealed. Whether she liked it or not, she had to stay with her mother who talked at length about all sorts of livelihood to support them. She planned to catch fish, trap crabs and frogs, and sell them in the town market. She planned to climb guava trees to pick their fruits and sell them in the town market. She planned to grate coconut meat, boil the shreds in brown sugar syrup until candied then sell them in the town market as well. For she had been an independent, fearless, and enterprising woman long before marriage. At a tender age, she had woven fishnets out of "number twenty" yarn for her own use and for sale to other fishermen. She had plowed the rice field, a menial job usually done exclusively by men. She had fought street brawls for her younger brothers and even older cousins and uncles.

5

Anacleta's father came after them the following day. There were several other times when her mother asserted her ideas to her father and to other people and got what she wanted. She was a strong woman who was unafraid and fiercely determined to bend anyone who did not agree with her. Thus she raised Anacleta, her only daughter, the way she thought every girl should be—fearless, enterprising and independent like her.

As soon as little Anacleta could sit, her mother taught her how to sell yams and limes while squatting on a gunnysack in the middle of an open market. Her mother took her to the grassy marshes and showed her how to make a fishing pole and line, dig for worm bait with her little hands, and cast for live frogs which they later sold to fishermen for their own use as fish baits. Anacleta grew up in this enterprising environment, learning to set price, count pesos and centavos, haggle, and make change. She was indoctrinated on the direct relationship of toiling under the rain or baking sun and earning money.

She also excelled in school, but her own independence took its toll, for one day she thought that her teacher was just wasting her time and she decided to drop out of school. She was only a second-grader then. "I already know two plus two equals four in the market," she declared, and she walked out of the classroom, never to return. She sold yams and limes full time, to the delight of her mother, who never really believed in formal schooling in the first place. Anacleta could already read, write, and do two digit sums. That was enough. She was equipped to grab the world by its tail.

Anacleta continued making a living in various other ways. After General Douglas MacArthur's forces liberated the Philippine Islands from Japanese occupation, Anacleta went to town and convinced surplus goods store owners to consign G. I. jackets to her. She hung two or three items on her shoulders and peddled them on foot. When her mother sent her for a vacation in a rich uncle's house in Manila, she babysat instead and worked as a messenger, walking to a popular Chinese restaurant to pick up lunches for the pressers at her uncle's dry cleaning shop.

I was the second of five children born to the union of Felix and Anacleta. They raised us in this hot and humid town which was home to many other farmers and fishermen. There, my brothers, sister and I played in dusty streets without fear of being trampled to death by motorized vehicles because there were none. Only occasionally, carts and sleds pulled by carabaos and horses plied the dirt roads, kicking clouds of dust in the air.

Father planted squash, eggplant, winged peas, and other vegetables in the moist fertile soil. He grew guava and tamarind trees, the leaves of which when boiled, produced medicinal water that mother forced us to drink to cure our stomach aches, or to sterilize scrapes and wounds. She used their sour fruits to flavor soups. Mother harvested from the small farm all year round for our meals and sold the excess in the town market. With the proceeds, she traded for rice, or she bought only necessities like sugar, salt, wooden clogs, pencils and paper for school, umbrellas, raincoats, and cotton clothing materials. She sewed our own clothes with an antique Singer sewing machine, for which she had bartered with a can of kerosene.

Father fished from streams and rivers that surrounded the town. I remember my endless fascination over the orange fish eggs, millions of them bound by transparent sac that mother pulled out of the mudfish belly to be boiled separately. Living up with tradition, she always served them with the fish head to Father, the head of the family. A tribute from one head to another.

Out of poverty came ingenuity. Mother designed toys both her sons and daughters could enjoy. She made wagons out of oval sardine cans and short milk cans. She fashioned boats, kites, and hats from newspapers, and utilized stones and driftwood for other toys. She showed us how to mold clay and shape mud after rains and taught us to build caves with sand during the dry season. For some reason, she never made dolls for Pag-asa and me, but come to think of it, we never asked her to make us some, either.

My siblings and I amused ourselves with activities of the mind. We played classroom and wrote and read aloud to each other. Outdoors, somehow, we could always find things to do: sift sand through our toes, throw pebbles to the river where people bathed and washed clothes, break a twig from a tree and spell words on the dirt, scoop live tadpoles from streams using the palm of our hands. Occasionally, with Mother, we watched Father rehearse with his amateur acting troupe a play that would be performed on a collapsible stage on a vacant lot across from the church. At the end of each rehearsal, Father took home the stage curtain for safekeeping until its next use. Mother tucked the thick, heavy, and neatly folded quilted curtain in one corner of our bare house.

At night, the whole family leaned side by side against the bamboo windowsill, and while the soft warm breeze rustled the leaves of trees and caressed our faces, we picked out the brightest stars in the black sky. Or, we watched the fireflies flicker naughtily as they played around the branches of the tamarind tree in front of our house. When it was time to call it a day, Mother spread for our bed a straw mat the size of the room. The straw was rough against the skin but it stopped the draft from flowing upwards through the bamboo slat flooring which was built on stilts ten feet above the ground. A symphony of the chirping of crickets, the rustle of bamboo leaves, the clap of raindrops against the streams, and the croaking of frogs, serenaded us to peaceful sleep. Thus my family led a simple, but nevertheless contented existence in the barrio, completely oblivious of other lifestyles. For all we knew, everyone in the world lived in bare nipa huts built on bamboo stilts!

Then suddenly, one damp evening in 1948, something disrupted our peace and quiet. A politician was shot and killed gangland-style in front of our house—blindfolded, hog-tied, and his naked frail body strapped to a tamarind tree. This incident exposed me to terror and human cruelty for the first time. I was only six years old then but the eyeless, mangled face of the dead man slumped in a pool of his own blood stuck in my mind. I still remember the heavy footsteps that rang through the walls of the nipa hut and the booming shouts of strange men.

"Turn off your lights!" a man yelled on top of his lungs, "Lie down, or we'll kill anybody in sight!"

Mother cut short our supper of boiled vegetables and steamed rice and Father blew the flame off the kerosene lamp suspended from the pitched thatched roof. No sooner had the room been darkened than three gunshots shattered the quiet night.

"Lie down on the floor, children!" Mother screamed, and she herself came crashing down.

Terrified, I hit the floor. The bamboo slats were hard and cold against my cheeks. I was sobbing with terror.

Mother, frantic about our safety, remembered someone had told her that soft, thick materials were bulletproof. She quietly crawled and reached for the stage curtain. While on her stomach, she struggled to cover us with it from head to toe. I felt her hand pat my back reassuringly. "The bullets won't penetrate this," she whispered.

The horror somehow vanished. Soon, sleep overcame fear, and when I woke up, the sun had already risen, its bright rays streaming through the wide-open window. When I looked out, I saw the village people, men in smocks and loose pants and women in *sarongs*, milling around the corpse.

The day would have passed like any other day of political unrest, but word spread like burning brushfire that Father had recognized the murderers while peering through a hole in the nipa wall of our house. News came, too, that if he stayed around the barrio any longer, the same killers would destroy him.

Father had indeed witnessed the killing. He actually recognized his cousin, the town's police chief, as the gunman who had shot the victim mercilessly right between the eyeballs. Knowing this, Father agonized for a decision whether to stay and testify against the killers or leave town and protect his family.

Father had always been a law-abiding citizen. He was incorruptible. He campaigned energetically for anyone whom he believed was deserving of public office. Politicians tried to, but could never buy his vote. He was dutiful. He felt it was his duty to see that the victim's plight be brought to justice. To do so, he must tell the court every bloody detail he had witnessed while peering through the nipa wall. He must testify against the killers. But he felt it was his responsibility, too, to raise his children away from harm, to see them grow up, finish high school, and get the professional degree he should have earned for himself. At last, after some profound soul-searching and much deliberation, Father reached an important decision: his children's future had priority. He must provide for that future. Besides, he could still be the star witness for the prosecution. The governor promised to pick him up and provide him bodyguard protection twenty-four hours a day when the trial began.

At the crack of dawn two days after the killing, my parents piled all of us and our worldly possessions on a big bamboo cart hitched to a carabao which they had borrowed from a relative. Pulled by the hardy beast over the muddy bumpy road, our family reached town. There we hopped on a bus that would take us to Manila, exact destination unknown.

The dilapidated bus overflowed with a mass of humanity, live animals, and fresh produce. The chickens, their legs tied with wires, flapped their wings in a valiant effort to free themselves. The pigs, also tied by their legs, shrieked continuously in protest of the indignity, terrifying little children seated on their mothers' laps. Wide hand-woven baskets filled to the brim with fresh fruits, vegetables, and fish completely blocked the aisle. Some men spread their legs to make room for them. Flies swarmed wildly about the produce, around and around the men's legs. Mother's antique Singer sewing machine, with its black ornate wrought-iron legs and pedal, stood on a spot at the back of the bus. Our box of clothes sat on top of its smooth varnished cover. Twice, the driver parked the bus on the shoulder of the highway, whereupon, the male passengers filed out and scampered about. Then, each one planted himself squarely behind a bush. When they climbed aboard the bus, smiles of relief adorned their faces, indicating they were ready once more to jockey into their uncomfortable positions.

I shared Mother's lap with Pag-asa near the window. Throughout the trip, we read aloud billboard advertisements for orange drinks and cigarettes on the highway, entertaining the mostly barely literate adult passengers. Silence came when the bus's rugged motion lulled my sister and me to sleep.

On the first afternoon in Manila, our family—hot, hungry, dirty, and exhausted—sought the house of Father's distant cousin who lived in a slum area. The cousin, a bent cadaverous man with a hacking tubercular cough, and a face mottled by life's hardships, ushered us to a room under a two-level shanty. There he gave us a big plate of cold rice and a tin can of coarse grains of salt and a jar of water. Mother moistened the rice with the water, mixed a dash of salt in it, and using our hands, we ate with gusto like dogs that hadn't been fed for days.

The walls of the shack were a patchwork of corrugated box cardboard, rusty sheet metals, and wood planks of odd shapes. The floor of the upper level was so low that Father, less than five-and-a-half feet tall, had to stoop when standing. He often forgot and banged his head accidentally against the beam. When the toddlers upstairs urinated, the urine leaked through the slats to our room and sometimes into our food. If it missed solid objects in its path, it created a small puddle on the packed dirt floor. Hundreds of such dwellings crowded one another on an area a stone's throw away from "smoky mountain," a smoldering garbage dump. There, the community residents scavenged, then sold pieces of wood, scraps of metals, and bottles. The neighborhood reeked of human waste.

My parents, sickened to their stomachs by the strong acrid air and cramping condition, asked for patience from us children. This would only be temporary, they assured us. To cheer us up, Mother declaimed, emulating an eloquent politician, "We are now in Manila, the premier city to which the four winds of the Philippines blow fortune seekers. Anyone who ever wants to leave his province of birth has only one destination in mind: Manila, the city where movies are made and schools of higher learning are built. Yes, ladies and gentlemen, this is the seat of high society. Anybody who can make it here can make it anywhere."

I stared enthralled at Mother as she continued her inspirational spiel about Manila where country farmers went to shake the mud off their feet to make money so plentiful they had to use wheelbarrows to haul them.

Mother immediately set out to find a place of our own to live. After a couple of days, she was able to announce: "I've found an ideal place—a bustling market where we can make our living. I'll sell fish."

"But where will you get the money?" Father asked, reluctantly. He was pushing our box of clothes around to make more space for circulation in the cramped room.

"My mother gave me twenty pesos," Mother proudly answered. "And I have already approached the market master. He said it's all right to build a stall where I'll sell, as long as it measures four meters square."

Right after Mother worked out the final details of negotiations with the market master, she summoned the whole family to the site. Like a small army, my parents and all of us children built the stall from pieces of wood and nails we bought or scavenged from all over town. Measuring four meters square, the room featured a counter window and a door facing the market building. The wooden floor, one big step above the ground was low enough to discourage pigs and dogs from probing underneath, yet high enough to prevent rain water from flooding it. To save on wall materials, we built against an existing stall. Ten such stalls, each connected to the other by a common wall, flanked both sides of the public market building. When smoke came out of one stall, the whole contraption resembled a beat-up locomotive.

I remember looking at the finished stall with some dismay. After all the wonders I had heard from Mother about Manila, and here we were, six of us jammed into another cubbyhole. In Bulacan, at least, the room was spacious, not suffocating; the air was fresh and wholesome, not putrid like this one. Fervently, I wished we had never left the province. I longed to go back to the wide open grass fields where the water buffaloes roamed lazily all day long.

Little did the market master know Mother had planned to use the stall as her family's living quarters; and that she would actually rent a table in the market building where she would sell fish. But when the market master, a bent and weathered man, discovered the arrangement, he amicably consented. After all, twenty other families were doing the same thing. "Just pay me five pesos more every month," he suggested with a wink. The extra money would go to his private slush fund.

After we settled in our new home, Mother, armed with her buy-and-sell trade and her sewing machine had no problem starting a livelihood. She just dove right into them like a duck would into a pond. But father, backed only by his farming experience, a skill not marketable in the city, could not find suitable employment. He had to figure out another way of earning a living. But fate might have had the blueprint shaping up for him. While building the stall, he developed interest in construction. He sought and got a job as a nail picker at a nearby construction project. From there on, he learned the basics of plumbing, electricity, steel bending, masonry, and other building skills. He moved on to street and public works projects such as dams and bridges and built his way up from being a peon to a respected construction foreman. With his inherent talent in mathematics, he quickly absorbed knowledge from plans and drawings prepared by architects and engineers. He became an expert in his own right and the construction professionals entrusted work to him with little or no supervision. Through the years, younger inexperienced men who were fresh out of technological schools came and went before his training eyes and he convinced himself he was an engineer just short of a piece of paper called a diploma. Therefore,

11

he vowed to have one of his children, it did not matter which one, go to engineering school to get that diploma, if he had to crawl to earn the money necessary to pay for the formal education. As his fate might have rubbed on mine, I, his second offspring, was nominated for that mission!

# Chapter 3

# The Birth
# of a Dream

**A** repulsive new environment dawned on me at the market ghetto. The stench of pigs butchered in the premises, of the rotting fish entrails thrown about, of the overripe fruit peels scattered on the slimy concrete slab, caused my head to ache for a while. The ear-piercing shrieks of dying pigs at four o'clock in the morning when butchering began, jerked me from sleep the first few times I heard them. When I went to use the public toilet, the concrete floor soaked in urine and excrement and a battalion of fat yellowish worms crawling in all directions appalled me! The gaseous fumes of decaying human waste knocked my senses, jolted me, and I staggered out and vomited uncontrollably.

A scruffy old man who wheezed with asthma supposedly maintained the community toilet but when he contacted dysentery in addition to his bleeding hemorrhoids, the market master fired him and padlocked the toilet for good. He nailed thick wood planks across its door. To stress his point, he posted a stern warning that anyone caught forcing entry would be fed to the worms. And I believed him. Since the slum residents were illegal squatters, the market management had no responsibility to furnish alternative comfort stations. No one dared complain, for fear of eviction. Left to my own devices to respond to the call of nature, I resorted to the bushes in the dark before sunrise or after sunset. During the monsoon season, I did it on a newspaper in the stall under the privacy of a sheet that covered me from head to toe, like a goblin. When the number was done, I wrapped the waste matter in sack-lunch fashion, set it loose on the street, and watched triumphantly under an umbrella, as the raging flood carried it to a drainage inlet.

A seventy-five-watt bulb hung from the ceiling to light the stall. It was the total electrical fixture allowed for a fixed monthly utility rate of a peso and a half. But Mother was a natural for resourcefulness. She discovered extension cords and electric irons. Why, she asked, should she use the primitive method of live charcoals inside a heavy metal flat iron and sweat her ears off? She pressed our clothes behind a line where sheets hung to shield her from the view of meter readers who occasionally made surprise visits to check on power stealing, a rampant practice in the ghetto.

Alongside the hanging lamp dangled a covered basket that held the family's food. The basket was our version of the cupboard and refrigerator. It protected the food from hungry dogs, cats, mice, and cockroaches. Mother usually put sugar in a covered jar, which she placed on a bowl of water. Only suicidal starving ants dared to cross the moat. At dinnertime, we ate on a portable dining table that Father had built. It was only one foot high so that we did not have to use chairs. After dinner, Mother wiped the table top with a wet rag and pushed the table sideways against the wall, leaving the square stall floor free of any obstacles for living room or bedroom use.

Savage crowding persisted in the city slum. Over a hundred residents, butchers, and vendors shared one water faucet that oozed very low pressure. The butchers and vendors maintained priority over its use during trading hours, which ran from seven to eleven in the morning. With trading over, the faucet was the hub of activities for the stall dwellers. They bathed, washed plates, pots, pans, and clothes. They hauled water for cooking. The waiting line of users carrying pails, bottles, jars, and kerosene cans that had been cleaned and improvised with wooden handles, and other imaginable containers, was usually long, and since the water pressure was low, tempers ran high. I became used to the sight of women pulling out each other's hair, or grown-up men chasing each other with long sharp knives to settle their turn at the faucet. When I found the chance, I washed up hurriedly at the faucet, fully clothed in a thick floral printed smock. Like all the women, I had to clean myself this way because if my wet garment showed any signs that my breasts had nipples, the ghetto men watched openly, their eyes glistening with lust, like hounds drooling after a bitch in heat. And yet, they bathed wearing only flimsy boxer shorts. This double standard of propriety aroused my curiosity and I once asked Mother why it was so, but she did not have an answer.

In front of the stall, Father dug a pit to which he assigned me the job of building the fire for Mother's cooking. I started the fire two hours ahead to dry the damp, if not soaking wet firewood. It was a hateful job—the business of constantly blowing my oxygen through a piece of one-inch diameter pipe to keep the embers glowing. At the end of the project, frustration and thick smoke often left my eyes red and stinging from tears and ashes.

The rich little old ladies of the Women's League adopted the market ghetto as their favorite charity during Christmas. They held fund drives for old clothes and canned goods which they gave away to the stall dwellers through a fat man dressed as Santa Claus. On our first Christmas here, Father taught me a lasting lesson on class-act poverty.

I remember the day a shiny car screeched in front of the market. The chauffeur held the door open and four middle-aged women dressed in slinky silks and dripping with jewelry filed out. He then opened the trunk. It bared gift-wrapped packages in assorted sizes. Immediately, the ghetto old-timers, coming from all directions, scrambled towards the women. The crowd was unruly. People crushed one another and held their hands up in the air, shouting, "Give me one!" or "One here!" When I found out they were jostling for giveaways, I braved the savage crowd. I managed to hustle one small package, which turned out to be a can of sardines. I proudly took it home to my parents. But Father nearly knocked me down with his reaction.

"Beggar!" His voice was terrible with anger. His words slashed through the air like a whip. He wouldn't touch the oval can of sardines, as though he feared it would soil his hands. He shot an outraged look at me. I stared at him, frozen, unable to move or say a word. "Return that alm, throw it or give it away," he commanded. "You ought to be ashamed of yourself begging like that. Don't ever do that again."

I moved a few steps backward, frightened, and still stunned. When the moment was right, I turned around, raced away and handed the can of sardines to the first person I saw.

From that moment on, I assumed my family was among the earth's elite poor; that we were a notch above paupers. If assistance looked like charity, we refused it, because accepting charity stripped us of dignity. Public charities at Christmas were hypocritical; they only licensed the rich people to make their day grand by patronizing the lowly poor.

In absolute poverty where the sun rose and set on survival, people either unlocked the vault of resourcefulness in making a living or stripped themselves of dignity and shame and begged for food during their waking hours. I knew of neighbors who plied a route in another part of town, knocking from door to door, pleading that a handful of rice grains be dropped into their small gunnysack. Yet for each neighbor who took the easy but shameful path, another flexed his muscles to wring out a few centavos from commerce. Men

15

scavenged empty bottles for resale to glass factories. Women worked as maids for rich people or at sweatshop factories where baby dresses were embroidered for export.

In time, my senses became numb to the sights and smells of poverty in the open market. Nothing bothered me anymore—not the toilet, not the savage fights at the faucet, not the wailing hogs. I blended with the other ghetto children who had already been pickled in a life of indigence.

In this place where not one centavo could be spared beyond rice and bare needs, ingenuity in seeking childish pleasures reigned supreme. We bounced around our "ball"—a dead pig's bladder that had been washed with salt, inflated until it was twice the size of a punching bag, tied tightly with a strong cord, and dried under the hot sun for weeks. The stench of the departed hog's urine clung to my hands for days after playing with the ball. We raced not toy cars but live spiders. The fastest spider to climb up a single strand of web won. After the races, we stashed the little creatures inside empty matchboxes for future events. Usually, they suffocated to death while we moved on to other sports and forgot about them completely. We played hide-and-seek inside and between tables in the market when trading hours were over. We scavenged rubber bands, and either strung them end to end for use as jump rope, or buried them individually in the ground for treasure hunt. For jacks we used pebbles and the rubber core of golf balls that had strayed from a nearby course. Going to the movies meant sitting outside of the dilapidated movie house of a community not far from the ghetto, listening to the sound tracks blasting out of the cracks on the wall.

And yet, these forms of entertainment did not quite provide the spark that would brighten my life. I longed for something beyond. In brutal poverty, it was easier to allow fantasy to take over my mind to cope with the harshness of daily realities. I established a pattern of escaping from the ghetto. I walked to the public school through a scenic route, a gravel road that wound around palatial homes. Uniformed gardeners were forever tending the manicured apple-green Bermuda grass lawns. The sight of chauffeured cars and servants dressed like nurses cultivated my fertile imagination. I imagined the chauffeur obediently picking me up from an exclusive school, and when I came home, nutty chocolate candy bars and grapes awaited me in the dining room. And dream on, I did, to childish contentment.

Unfortunately, some dreams ended abruptly and brutally. My classmates discovered that I lived in a four-meter-square market stall instead of a conventional house and they named me "market pig." In school, they passed little notes to me, asking if I could write the lyrics of an imaginary song titled "A Little Pig in the Market." When I recited in class, they whispered "market pig" audibly to distract me. At first I did not mind the brand, but one day during a traditional religious procession and pageant of biblical queens, my classmates spotted me among the participants. They taunted me. They chanted "market pig, market pig" until I could not bear it any longer. I broke out of the parade and dashed home crying.

Mother, who was never notably religious, was puzzled at first. "What was all that for?" she looked up and asked. She was sewing a dress. A thimble capped her middle finger and she was surrounded with self-designed patterns cut out from old newspapers. "Why did you abandon the group?"

I sobbed and blew my nose repeatedly, Words would not come out of my lips. Finally, they tumbled out. "My classmates have been calling me market pig for a long time now. Tonight they even shouted it in public. When are we ever going to live in a real house like everyone else?" I was angry and my voice demanded an answer.

Not a ripple showed on the face of my mother, this tiny woman of steel. She had told me before that as a child, she had been a vicious bully, fighting any one who crossed her. She had often warned us not to come home crying from brawls; that if we could not defend ourselves, we should stay home and play by ourselves; that there were enough of us to form two teams for whatever game we wanted to play. "Listen, and listen good," she said through her teeth, stressing each word very carefully, her pointer wagging at me. "We are not moving anywhere just because some children called you market pig. You are better than they are in school; they're jealous. Some people will do anything when they are jealous. Why did you not fight them? What have I been telling you and your brothers and sister? If you can't fight out there, stay home."

I stared, appalled, at my unsympathetic mother. Her voice had been like a branding iron that left black scorched marks in my mind. *If you can't fight out there, stay home.* My sobs trailed off. After that incident, I was never entirely a little girl again. I lived in the ghetto but my heart belonged somewhere else. Poverty surrounded me but I despised every part of it. Imbedded in my mind was a burning ambition to step outside its limits.

I rode higher on air castles, imagining a big house in the rich people's subdivision. It had an airy room with a bed all for myself. It also had a bathroom where I could scrub my naked body in privacy. Its refrigerator bulged with tender meats and fancy foods. But in spite of my daydreams, reality was there, as big as life. At night, all six fully-clothed bodies of our family lay side by side on the floor, sharing one giant-sized sheet sewn from several flour sacks, and under one huge netting that protected us from bloodsucking mosquitoes and other live creatures that fought for space.

One night, a rat the size of a fat Idaho potato lost its way and found itself trapped inside the mosquito netting. It scampered about in confusion, trying to escape. In the process, it scurried across my face. Its sharp nails woke me up. When it dawned on me what was happening, I leaped to my feet, horrified. My voice exploded like a grenade and awakened the whole family. All six people jumped up. A wild chase ensued inside the netting. In spite of disorientation from sleep, the humans won over the beast. Mother sliced and disemboweled the rat with the blow of a machete. At the end of the furious battle, I huddled in one corner of the stall, shaking, my hand covering my mouth, sick at the sight of the rat's blood and guts stuck to the mosquito netting. Mother cleaned up the mess and summoned us all back inside the transparent protective enclosure. She carefully tucked the edges of the netting once more under the straw mat. "Do you see how tight it is? Even the cockroaches won't make it inside now," she thoughtfully reassured me.

As if there was no space problem, my parents even managed to produce my baby sister, and this drove me to the limits of hatefulness. During rainy days, wet diapers sewn from bleached flour sacks hung from a series of clotheslines inside the stall. Even though I was only eight then, I remember having to stoop to avoid the damp cloths from touching my face. My poor innocent little sister Ruby! She hadn't the slightest notion how much I resented the intense discomfort she had brought into my world, which caused me to swear in my tender mind never ever to get married and have babies. She and Mother maintained exclusive use of the floor as their bed twenty-four hours a day. Fortunately there was school, which doubled as shelter from sun and rain, otherwise my waking hours would have been spent miserably in the dank stall that reeked of baby's wastes. I fervently wished for the years to rush forward so that bright sunlight could sterilize the stall.

Soon my little sister Ruby was toddling and Mother took down the clotheslines. I could see the stall's ceiling once again, not that it was a great sight to behold. Like other tiny children in the ghetto, Ruby defecated and urinated on the dirt road in front of the stall. To help raise her consciousness of the neighborhood's accepted hygienic practices, I showed her how to scoop dirt with her bare hands to cover the waste matter to shield it from the flies. Sometimes, if she was lucky, she did not have to lift a finger. Two or three pigs waited anxiously behind her, prepared to fight over the feces for their meal.

In two more years, other things of greater importance took over my life, like thoughts of where to go for high school. I enrolled in a public high school in the adjacent town where no one knew where I lived; where I flung myself furiously into learning as revenge against the ghetto. The less time I spent at home, the happier I felt. The library became my spacious living room until time came for me to go home, to eat and sleep. The cafeteria served as my comfortable dining room. It gave me a heavenly feeling to eat sitting on a chair in front of a normal table using spoon and fork. I imagined myself in a banquet surrounded by important people, dining on food possible only in the colorful pages of magazines, like baked ham covered with pineapple slices studded in place by brown spices that looked like little nails. But bits and pieces of real life appeared when I had to eat my lunch that Mother had wrapped in fire-softened banana leaves. It usually consisted of cold rice and a fried eggplant or a small mackerel boiled in vinegar and ginger root. During recess, I walked to the nearby government-maintained botanical garden, my imaginary big lawn, where I filled my lungs with wholesome clean air. None of my classmates knew my secret fantasies of luxury and comfort, for once in their midst, I was an ebullient character who delighted in clowning around and making them laugh at my own expense, and who seemed content with the world.

Mathematics and physics consumed my passion, an affair with numbers that developed from a painful experience in grade school, when my third grade teacher asked me for the product of eight and seven and I did not know the answer. It must have been one of her PMS days, for instead of helping me, she had blasted: "Get out! Don't return unless you know how to multiply every number by eight!"

Horrified, I went home crying and told Father the story. To my surprise, he simply smiled. He cleared his throat to lecture. "That's no problem." He proceeded to teach me the use of the multiplication chart of a spiral notebook. "Just follow a number from column to column, and presto, you have the answer."

That night, I did not sleep until I had mastered Father's magic formula. Prepared to prove my expertise to my teacher the following morning, I charged into school, full of confidence. My eyes dared the teacher to ask me any multiplication question. I was ready to knock her dead with my knowledge. But much to my disappointment, she ignored my presence completely!

Father's encouragement pushed my interest so much deeper into mathematics, into the mysteries of high school algebra, geometry, and physics. But then I realized during those days the difference between a boy who was good in these subjects, and a girl who excelled just as well. As a girl, I had the makings of a woman and women's hands were tied, restraining them from conquering their own fates. Tradition sentenced the women into a fourth of a lifetime of servitude to their parents, and as mother substitutes to their brothers, and when they married, into a bondage with their husbands for the rest of their breathing years. Fortunately, I had descended from a weird family with at least three known generations of sturdy women and their men who did not, or could not, make an issue of them. However, in the sphere outside my family, the tradition continued to be perpetuated. The unfair advantage of the boys, who grew up to become men, surfaced clearly on my first attempt at competing in a mathematics contest.

The Department of Education held an annual mathematics contest where each school entered its best students. At my school, I passed all the pre-qualifying rounds with flying colors. Two boys, named Niño and Jose qualified too, but they were distant second and third. The three of us became the final representatives at the contest and we bragged about our achievements until the reality of rigid preparation sobered us. For three weeks, the math teacher, our coach, and the two boys and I stayed after class to cram for the big event. After each practice session, I came home exhausted, but always anxious to share with Father my excitement about the forthcoming contest. Whereupon, he repeated his stories of how he and Luis Taruc always returned from different towns triumphant from math competitions, and I listened, my eyes aglow with intense admiration. His stories of glory always titillated my imagination and sent me into a charmed sleep, dreaming of a whopping victory in the contest. When I woke up the following morning, I could hardly wait again for the next practice session.

On the eve of the contest, our coach assembled the boys and me for final instructions. "We will not practice anymore tonight," she announced, shuffling her papers. "Go home and get plenty of sleep, and tomorrow eat a good breakfast and you'll all be fresh and bright and effective."

The boys and I listened intently, soaking in every word of advice. Feeling confident and well prepared, we were all ready to charge into the arena in the morning.

The teacher continued. "Be at the auditorium tomorrow at seven." Then she turned to the boys. "You two will be our contestants. Celia will be alternate."

Alternate! The word jolted me to attention. "What do you mean alternate?" I asked, my eyes wide and probing.

The teacher cleared her throat. She tapped my shoulder and said, "That means you'll compete only if either Jose or Niño does not show up or gets sick."

I was crushed. The winner's crown that I had placed squarely on my head in my dreams tumbled down my feet. "Why didn't you tell me in the beginning?" I demanded, trying to keep my voice from breaking. "That's not fair." I wanted to say more, but didn't. "Thou shalt respect your teachers" was not in the Ten Commandments but it might as well have been number 5a for parents impressed it in the minds of their children.

"Boys are calmer than girls," the teacher answered sourly. "They can take pressure, so they'll be better contestants for our school. We want winners. I didn't tell you in the beginning because I wanted you to prepare just as hard in the unlikely event that you did have to participate." These were words from the lips of a *female* geometry teacher.

So that closed my case. Without the benefit of a fair trial, I had been condemned to the cursed fate of a loser because of the belief that all girls had the inherent characteristic of being emotional and flappable, not cool and collected. I went home brokenhearted, and told Father what happened. He thought, then wrinkled his nose as a gesture of distaste for an unwelcome fact. After a brief moment of additional mulling, he spoke, his voice holding a note of resignation, "Show up at the contest anyway."

The following day, the auditorium teemed with excitement while I sulked in the front row among the people watching the contest churn out winners and losers. Jose and Niño were among the casualties. Our school lost. However, at the end of the last event, the master of ceremonies announced an important news: there would be a special geometric construction event.

A tap on my shoulder brought my attention back into focus. I looked up and saw my teacher. She was smiling. "We'll field you on this one," she said, with a wink. "Go on and give them hell!"

Up the stage I ran, or hopped, I was not sure which, the force of lust for competition propelling me. Once on stage, I took a sweeping glance at my opponents to size them up. I estimated there were about fifteen and they were all boys. I was *the only girl*.

The host's voice filled the hall again: "Contestants, get ready. Within one minute, construct a rhombus, given one side and an included angle." He studied the second hand of the official timer. "Get set, and.... go!"

I seized my wooden compass, straightedge, and a piece of chalk. Faster than my heartbeat, my hands flew as I drew the line, the angle, and finally the rhombus. Upon completion of the figure, I swung around to face the audience, then the judges. I saw my classmates and the teachers clapping their hands wildly, screaming and waving at me the victory sign. Then the verdict was announced: I had beaten the other contestants by a good margin of time. I had won first prize!

## Celia Ruiz-Tomlinson

For my achievement, I received a fountain pen made in Germany, a set of stainless steel drawing instruments made in Switzerland, and the audience's thundering applause that would ring in my ears for years to come. I floated in euphoria from the stage all the way home and proudly presented my windfall to my parents. While inspecting my prize, Father's eyes glistened with pride. "You have done well, my daughter," he said in a low, moderated voice. "You crushed a bunch of boys on their own turf. You ought to be very proud of yourself."

I went to bed that night greatly elated. Words of praise are sweet to a child. I felt pleased with myself, and imagined I was not to be taken lightly by anyone. The following morning, Mother would not be outdone in bragging about my achievement. With me in tow, she galloped from stall to stall and insisted that the other ghetto dwellers see the prize. "Feel the cool stainless steel of these little things," she said, as she urged everyone to inspect the drawing instruments. The neighbors had no idea what the compass and inking pens were for, but they obliged anyhow out of curiosity.

My victory in the mathematics contest turned out to be a key that would unlock unknown challenges in my life and destiny.

# Chapter 4

# The Decision

Father often played with me when I was little. I'd be on the floor bouncing a ball made from old socks. He'd write a letter, pretend like he forgot how to spell a certain word, and ask me to spell it. I'd oblige and his eyes would widen in mock surprise, and he'd put on a great show of being impressed with my ability. Thus, he nourished my growing interest in the written and spoken word. As I grew into adolescence, the bounds of my dream world expanded in direct proportion with my voracious appetite to read and write. Stories of exotic places fascinated me and lured me to take the qualifying test to join the staff of our school newspaper just so I could have a chance to go to a school-sponsored conference of journalism students held annually in a different island. I was admitted as a reporter and columnist. At this entry-level position, I knew it would be tough to compete against the editors, as far as winning a spot on the delegation team. But I was acutely aware that being on the staff, no matter how humble the position, gave me a good shot at being considered. I figured my chance, as a member of the staff, was one hundred percent better than if I did not belong.

The day of the selection of delegates came soon enough and it made sense that the school picked all the major editors. Although I had expected that outcome, somehow I could not help but feel a jolt of defeat. In my tender mind, my only chance to see the world outside Manila was lost and gone forever. When I arrived home that day from school, I idly browsed through the pages of the geography book. My fingers marched across the map of the southern island where the conference would be held, whisking me across vast green plantations and rugged mountains. My dreams of riding in a vessel that sailed for days on the Pacific Ocean and of sighting flipping whales and verdant outcroppings were dashed. I secretly wanted to cry.

It turned out, however, that all was not lost. Something happened that would change the course of events in my favor. On the day of the delegation's departure, the society editor caught a bad case of stomach flu and at the last minute, the school officials replaced her with me. With only a couple of hours to prepare for the departure, I slithered all the way home on cloud nine, and there, while packing my clothes, I danced my excitement away to an imaginary bouncy beat. The stall floor grated and creaked. The lamp swung like a pendulum.

My second-fiddle appointment brought me more than excitement. It released an unstoppable force within me. I burst with so much vim and vigor that I felt I could jog for hours without exhausting myself. All the way to the conference in a city in a lush island reached only through a three-day boat ride from Manila, my euphoria carried on. At the conference, my genuine joy permeated the literary piece for which I won a bronze medal in the feature-writing contest. I wrote in almost palpable exhilaration, a crisp unabashed account of my excitement about the trip and my expectations from it! When the delegation returned to Manila, our school held a special program to pin the medal on me.

The competitive campus activities made high school years rush forward and before I knew it, it was time to graduate. I received my diploma with mixed emotions. Both happy and scared, I wondered what my parents had in mind for me. Nothing much had changed. We still lived in the ghetto, but with our grown bodies, our stall's floor space had become smaller. As if the room could take more, my sister Pag-asa breezed through an unsuccessful marriage and brought home an infant son. Her elopement while attending secretarial school burned out my parents so badly that they exploded when they heard the word "college." What was in store for me? Those nagging thoughts persisted all through that summer vacation.

With only one more week left before the deadline for college registration, Father suddenly brought up the subject of furthering my education, something that people in our economic class never heard of. As the family squatted on the floor around the portable wooden table with a plateful of steaming rice and dried salted fish one evening, he popped the question: "Are you interested in going to college or not?" It sounded like an ultimatum. Shocked, my lips parted to make way for a response.

To my surprise, Mother answered with the speed of lightning. "She is not going anywhere. She will hunt for a job, earn money, and help us move out of this dump." The finality in her voice horrified me. She alternated chewing and discoursing.

## Don't Ever Tell Me You Can't

In Mother's lifetime sphere of buying and selling, money moved everything and everything was either black or white. As the person who controlled the family's purse strings, she spoke eloquently about money that bought food for eight hungry mouths. Money was paid for the electric bulb that lit the stall at night. For money, the jeepney driver transported her daily to and from the fish wholesalers in a nearby town. Why, money bounced the world! For the life ahead of her, all Mother wanted was to save enough money to build a conventional house that would shield the blooming figures of her daughters from the lusting eyes of men.

"Ruby will be bleeding in a couple more years, and between her and Celia, we will need more clotheslines inside the stall to hang their sanitary belts and napkins," she said, referring to old shirts and recycled flour sacks.

I cringed in embarrassment at Mother's candor. I felt like she had stripped me of my clothes and exposed my reproductive organs.

She continued. "More than anything else, what we need is lots of money so that we can buy us a house and have some privacy for these girls." She hammered on and on about the virtues of money. As long as the source was legitimate, for Mother the name of the game was money, money, and money.

Father flung his arms up in the air, accidentally tossing a few grains of steamed rice. "Money? Is that all you can think of. Your daughter might want to go to college and get a degree and make something good out of herself. Think of it."

"College!" Mother spat out the word like vinegar and covered her ears with the palm of her hands. "No, no, no, no, and a thousand times no. Your daughter is also a woman who will only get married later on, like Pag-asa. She just wasted our money. Didn't she elope before the semester ended? A baby boy—that's all we got out of college. Forget about degrees for these girls. We'll wait for our sons to grow up, and then we'll talk about college. You think about it."

I cowered under the crossfire of my parents as their accumulated conflict in principles spewed out. Mother, the second-grade dropout who had grown up selling yams and limes, continued to harp upon me earning money as soon as possible. She had nothing against school if it were free. But even if it were, she rattled about all the incidental expenses related to it, like clothes, shoes, transportation, lunches. Then there would be books, notebooks, pens, inks, and endless school supplies. After all the schooling was said and done, the student would graduate and hunt for work to earn money.

"Why go through all that trouble when it's also money a college graduate looks for, anyway," she asserted, loudly. She pinched a piece of fish, placed it on top of a small mound of rice, picked up the whole thing and shoved it to her mouth. While she chewed the food, I could tell from her eyes she was thinking of her next choice of words, getting ready again for another tirade on the advantages of earning money here and now.

Father, who had lost his chance at higher education because of a damnable gambling incident, insisted that I go to college. Dissatisfied with a plain laborer's life, he determined that his children would not grow up like him with calluses in his hands and sixth grade education between his ears. In his vision of the good life, there were air-conditioned offices such as the ones he helped build, desks, stiffly starched white collars, a sprawling house. If a person really succeeded in a profession there would be a car and a chauffeur, and at each child's birthday party, a whole suckling pig roasted to a golden brown, with an apple in its parted jaws, imposed on a scrumptious feast for two hundred relatives and friends.

"A professional degree is the only passport to the good life. Making money would not be as difficult," he stressed, equally as loud.

Silence fell over the rest of the family. Only the sound of chewing and swallowing could be heard.

Suddenly Father's voice exploded once more, but this time with a hint of concession. "And what kind of a job do you think she can do other than becoming a housemaid for the rich people up the hill?" Finished with his meal, he dipped his right hand into a coffee can that was half-filled with water, to wash the food off it. He looked around, and finding no clean rag to dry his hand, he wiped it on the lap of his soiled pants.

Mother sensed victory and responded quickly. "She can work permanently as a salesgirl in the bookstore of one of my wealthy customers. She can start any time."

I broke out in gagging coughs, the way a person did when a fish bone got stuck in the throat. I hated that job. I had tried it sometime back and had lasted exactly eight hours. In my memory, that was the day when five o'clock seemed to refuse to arrive, and when it finally did, I swore I'd never have anything to do with selling used books again. Used books that made the rounds of many different hands! Some even had cockroach eggs pressed between their pages! But I kept the words to myself. It would not be proper, by custom, to barge into my parents' argument.

Noticing my coughing hysteria, Mother and Father turned their attention to me. Then they turned their faces towards each other. Their eyes locked. They thought, and agreed to make her decide. After all, it was her life. What was everybody's problem?

"What do you want to do?" It was Father who asked the critical question directly.

"If we can afford it, I'd really prefer to go to college and get a degree," I said hurriedly, lest I lose my chance to speak up. With that, I gulped a glass of water.

Father sighed with relief and rose from the floor. He smiled. "Did you hear that? Your daughter wants to go to college and make something good out of herself, he said, looking down victoriously at Mother, then shifting his eyes to me, he asked, "What will you study, child?"

Caught off-guard, I hesitated. I had not thought that far ahead. I quickly searched my brain for courses that young people went to college for. Finding no specific discovery, words just tumbled out of my mouth. "I don't know. Maybe teaching. Journalism. Nursing. What do you think?"

Mother's face paled with controlled anger. She frowned. "Did you hear that? She doesn't even know what she wants. And you're going to spend money on her?" she asked with sarcasm. She reached for my brother's dirty shirt behind her and used it as a rag to wipe the food scraps off the table.

Father made no reply. Instead, he looked down at me—his eyes glossed over with disappointment. "Teaching? Journalism? Why those? Take something solid. Get a degree that will earn you a good living—like engineering. Be a civil engineer."

Civil engineer! The words rang through my inquisitive mind. My eyes lit up. I had no idea what a civil engineer did but it sounded rather important. A woman civil engineer. I had never heard of one. Suddenly, the glory of victory in the math contest flashed through my mind. *You crushed a bunch of boys on their own turf.* I remembered how the taste of the heady wine of triumph had filled me with a warm bracing exuberance. I yearned to feel it all over again. The desire impelled me to a firm decision. "That's a great idea!" I exclaimed, brimming with zest. "I want to become a civil engineer." And I clasped the idea to my heart.

Mother's jaws fell. She also did not know what a civil engineer was but she had never heard of a girl civil engineer either. "A girl becoming a civil engineer? That's about the dumbest idea since World War One," she said flatly. "You're not making sense, you two. You've both gone out of your minds." She picked up the table and slammed its flat side against the wall. In spite of her inner strength, Mother was a good deferential wife to Father. She had mastered the art of making him feel as if he made all the decisions in the house. She watched her words when talking to him about the family finances, focusing them to demand instead of his and her contributions to the supply. She had always been the main breadwinner.

Pag-asa swept the rest of the crumbs from the floor, creating room once more for the straw mat and pillows and mosquito netting for another night of sleep for the family.

## Celia Ruiz-Tomlinson

The decision to send me to engineering school in 1958 actually drew the family together. As the family sat on the straw mat, Father, by then a street construction foreman, vowed to work longer hours to earn enough money to support me. Mother made plans to supplement her fish vending by sewing clothes for other people at night. Rodolfo, the older of my two brothers agreed to sit out a year after graduating from high school. Pag-asa looked forward to getting her own table in the market to sell fish, the trade Mother had taught her after her marriage failed, to support herself and her son and lighten the family's burden.

"I will walk to Suya's store to read the clock for you in the mornings," my younger brother, Godofredo volunteered. The whole family looked at each other in amazement. Suya, the Chinese who owned a grocery store seven blocks away, was the only person who had a timepiece: a small alarm clock. Out of the kindness of his heart, he had it placed strategically on a shelf at the back wall so that it was close enough to be read, but not touched, by the ghetto people. Little brother hit the need for correct time right on the mark. The ghetto was a timeless place. There were no clocks, only calendars. No hours and minutes, only days of the week. Events told the approximate time, which seemed to suffice. Dying pigs shrieked and pierced the residents' ears around four o'clock in the morning. Fresh fish and produce sellers arrived somewhere around seven. The market came to life with brisk trading by nine. The janitor hosed the place down near eleven and at approximately two o'clock the postman, who knew every adult resident by name, delivered mails that had been addressed simply "Public Market, Makati."

Little brother got the right idea. As a college student, I'd be joining an outside civilization that moved in accordance with the hands of the clock. I'd need to know exact times now so I could determine when to get ready for school and when to start walking the ten blocks to the bus turn-around station.

The family applauded younger brother's choice of valuable contribution to my proposed schooling.

My baby sister, now eight, looked inquiringly at our faces, wondering what was happening. But if she had the slightest idea about the family project, with the spirit of altruism pervading the room, she might have also offered to contribute something in her own little way.

To pay for my initial expenses, my parents sold the pig, which they had fattened, from crude molasses and garbage scavenged from the market. Then they bought a new litter to be fattened again and sold to the butchers for the following semester. Impo, Mother's mother, who frowned at the idea of school in general, nevertheless, opened her heart and pocketbook and donated a few pesos to the cause. Using the money, Mother and I bought me a good pair of shoes. Mother sewed a couple of dresses to tide me over until she knew exactly what school uniform she had to make.

Father pegged on me his bright, smoldering hopes for the future. "Five years from now," he said repeatedly to the family, while looking out of the window to the far horizon, "Celia will be a civil engineer. She will make good money like Engineer Banaag." He was referring to the wealthy president of Banaag Construction, who had the most contracts with the government. He owned a sprawling house with a security guard and a fleet of vehicles on the other side of the market. "We will be able to borrow money from the bank and build us a real house up the hill. Celia will design and I will build it."

Amidst all the growing heavy expectations, I could feel the family's pressure pinning me to the ground. Father's constant fantasizing about my "degree" forced me to wear vivid war paints to face the forthcoming challenge. As the school opening approached with frighteningly uncontrollable speed, I tried to hype myself into a knight with shining armor and a civil engineering degree, ready to liberate every member of the family from the structured box of poverty. Nothing to it, I psyched myself up. Go to engineering school for five years, get the diploma, pass the board, find a job, borrow money from the bank, design a house. It seemed easy. Fact of the matter was, deep within me huddled a shrinking, trembling, stiffly scared child.

I did not realize how truly scary it was until the first day in engineering school. When I entered the walled campus of Mapua Institute of Technology, the sight of a virtual tidal wave of men inundated me. It was as though the whole male population of the Philippine Islands was there, milling about the campus. For a brief moment, I stood at the gate, frightened, my feet tarred to the street. I considered turning around, grabbing the first bus, and forgetting about this engineering bit. But my feet remained rooted to the earth. Visions of contorted angry faces of my family hovered about me. The tuition fee that had already been paid, the fat pig that had been sacrificed, the planned exodus from the slum in five years—they all appeared like hideous monsters ready to swallow me alive. The disappointment I would see in Father's face haunted me. I closed my eyes tightly and took a deep breath. The call of duty rose inexorably in me; I could not find the strength to turn around. I must become a civil engineer.

Summoning all the courage I could muster, I braced myself to cross what appeared to be a mob ready to lynch me. I sucked in my breath and ran or walked; I am not sure which, across the campus. Did I actually feel it, or was it only my imagination that several thousand pairs of eyes were focused on me? When I reached the classroom, a roomful of men nearly overwhelmed me again, but thank goodness I spotted four young women seated in the front row. Instinctively, I sat next to them. I tried to draw from their experiences, hopefully to reaffirm my own. Immediately, I learned the details of the other women who, like myself, were venturing through a moat to a fortress long controlled by men.

Isabel Lee was Chinese with skin like polished glass; baby-fine brown hair tied in a ponytail, and delicate pretty features. Neatly dressed in an expensive silk dress, she possessed an unmistakable air of affluence. The daughter of the owners of a factory that produced chemicals for hair shop permanents, she spoke fluent English and Mandarin and said she was headed for chemical engineering. She decided on this herself, following her older brother's example.

The second girl had an angular face and wore thick glasses, making her look more serious than the rest. Her lips curved downward, her ears stuck out slightly although she had tried to cover them with her permed hair. She proudly mentioned that she had graduated on top of her class in the southernmost island of the Philippines. She, too, was from a wealthy family that owned a corn plantation. She wanted to become a chemist, a profession suggested by her father.

The third girl was tall and thin, quite masculine in appearance, and had a deep voice. Her straight hair had been cut like a boy's. Her front teeth were a gold bridge of ill fit. When she smiled, the ends of the bridge formed a sharp angle with her natural teeth. In her low voice, she mentioned her family owned and operated several fleets of jeepneys in a Manila suburb. She said she was majoring in civil engineering, an idea her father had planted in her mind.

Then there was the beauty, Guadalupe Ramos. A graduate of an exclusive parochial school, her long thick hair matched the pitch black of her eyes. When she smiled, which she did often, deep dimples graced her rouged smooth cheeks. She wore lipstick which made her even more attractive. In a soft honeyed voice she talked about her father, a noted civil engineering consultant, who wanted her to follow in his footsteps.

I was relieved at the discovery that we all had gasped at the sight of the sea of men at the campus gate and that we shared the same anxieties and misgivings. Except for Isabel Lee, who smiled more than she talked, each of us wondered what we had gotten ourselves into.

Having studied the girls, I took a long critical survey of myself. How did I rate with these women who, like myself, either by choice or parental suggestion or both, were trying to buck tradition? I formed a mental picture of the girl with round tanned face and long straight

30

black hair, who stared at me critically each time I looked at the mirror. From top of head to shoulder bones, I was an ugly spectacle when propped side by side with Isabel and Guadalupe. But I estimated I towered a whole head over them, and my small waist, full hips and abundant backside gave their uneventful figures a little run for their money. The two other girls' harsh, homely features would trigger the mercury of the barometer of physical appearance downward, a couple of notches below my mark. After thoroughly rating the charms of each of us women, it came home to me as a great blow that I was, wow, really average in looks. A plain "Pinay." I was possessed of neither absolutely smashing beauty nor striking ugliness. In family riches, however, I was totally outclassed. An eddy of envy sank my spirits when I imagined the women relishing the lives of pampered princesses in their parents' luxurious mansions or in expensive boarding houses. I bet none of them ever heard of family life in a market stall where toilet and bathroom activities demanded ingenuity on a daily basis.

The bell buzzed, breaking my train of thoughts. It signified the start of the engineering orientation class. The hissing of conversations came to an abrupt halt. All eyes focused on a limping man with a cane, who entered the room. His thick eyebrows darkened his narrow face. His neck was short and stiff. When he turned his head to glance at the hallway, his whole small-boned torso went with it. As soon as he reached the table in the front, he laid his cane on top of the table and opened his leather briefcase. He dug out an eraser and a few pieces of chalk. He turned his back to the class and printed his name GARCIA on the board, using long downward strokes. Having completed this, he faced the students again, and while wiping the chalk dust from his hands, he shot one long examining look at the women in the front row. "So you girls want to become engineers?" he roared, as he directed his question to Guadalupe. "Why?

Shocked, Guadalupe fluttered her long eyelashes and opened and shut her mouth but the words never came out. She looked around fearfully like a cornered animal. The professor seized the opportunity to whip her with the final lash to bring her down on her knees. He grabbed and slapped his wooden cane against the table top, with a resounding thud. Guadalupe's shoulders jerked.

"Hell!" he yelled, his eyes skimming one woman's terrified face after another. "You don't even know why you are studying engineering. Why don't you girls just stick to dressmaking?" He looked at the men to orchestrate a response.

As though prompted by the cue, a wave of laughter from the male students overflowed the classroom. I lowered my head, shut my eyes, and held my breath. My body trembled with a mixture of fright and rage.

31

## Celia Ruiz-Tomlinson

All in one moment, I wanted to turn back the hands of time to the night I had clasped to my heart the idea of becoming a civil engineer to undo everything. And yet, suddenly possessed of intense self-righteous indignation, I wanted to mow down the men for such barbarity. A resolve gelled in my subconscious. There would be no looking back, and I braced myself for a long hard fight for a space in the engineering field.

# Chapter 5

# The Long Lonely Climb

hile it was tough, early life in engineering school actually prepared me for the rough battle ahead as a professional engineer in the Philippines and the United States, I grant that. I'll never forget the first time I witnessed harassment.

The physics professor had the spit-and-polish image of an old West Point graduate: stocky, gray-haired, with a level gaze, and a posture as erect as a bayonet. He walked about the front of the classroom with an unmistakable air of authority, his eyes like a powerful searchlight scanning the room. When they locked with mine, a chill crept up my spine. Trouble, I whispered fearfully. But then he moved them on to the beauty. I sighed in relief; I felt a heavy burden lifted from me.

"Explain Newton's Law of Motion," he commanded Guadalupe, in a voice that would have startled a platoon.

Guadalupe stood up reluctantly and babbled, missing more than hitting the subject matter.

Sensing her panic, the professor rushed forward, lowered his face, practically breathed on hers, and grunted, "You have time to make up your face with fancy cosmetics but you don't have time to study your lessons. Why don't you just get married and start having babies? That's easier." He straightened his back and directed his next statement to the men in the back row. "One of you guys, marry this girl and get her out of here."

The men's boisterous laughter rocked the classroom.

Guadalupe's humiliation made my stomach contract with a cold prickling urgency. The fear of direct personal attack gnawed at me. What if the professor targeted me? Slow death from shame, I thought, and the end of a mercifully short-lived career. I took a mental note of the professor's language. He had made a big deal out of Guadalupe's facial make-up. Henceforth, I shunned lipsticks, eyebrow pencils, and even talcum powder. I slicked my hair into a tight ponytail to go with my naked face, wore drab clothes, and worked hard at being inconspicuous as a female student. I did not tuck my blouse in my skirt waist to play down my full figure. Flat shoes rounded off my artless wardrobe. And I marched to school each day fully prepared to answer the professors' questions.

At the end of the horrible first semester, engineering school was like a giant colander with enormous holes. Four out of every five students did not measure up to the demands of the course, fell through the openings, and were washed into other less exacting endeavors. Guadalupe led the procession of the women throwing in the towel. She told me about her father's disappointment, but she could no longer endure the professors' harassment; that she wanted to live the normal life of a woman. She enrolled in another school to study secretarial courses. When sophomore year started, two other girls dropped out for good. They, too, had mentioned they could not take the insults anymore and decided to do something else with their lives.

I survived, as did Isabel Lee, who later graduated on top of the Chemical Engineering class of 1964. But then, Isabel Lee was unfairly endowed, the perfect example of life's inequities. She was pretty, intelligent, healthy, and wealthy all at the same time. She just had it all. Sometimes I wondered why, but precious time was better used not in envying other people's fortunes but in pursuing other worthwhile efforts, like studying.

Despite my all-out efforts, however, I did not completely succeed in ducking the darts of insults shot by the professors. One time when I scored low on a test, the professor announced it in class, like airing my underwear in public, then said to me indulgently, "What makes you think you can be a civil engineer? Quit now and save time and your parents' money."

It was one of the cruelest moments I had to endure, but it made me realize something very important. The professor's words did not kill me. Instead, it strengthened me. Even that cold contraction in my stomach vanished. Instead, his unsolicited advice stirred raw defiance within me. Quit engineering because of one low score? Callousness had set in.

The male students had their own way of embarrassing or harassing the women. Between classes, when I or any of the women was within hearing distance from any group of two or more, the men exchanged lewd, graphic sex jokes and stories, then stared at us to see if they succeeded in offending us. Usually, the other woman left. I didn't. I stayed until the men had expended their reservoir of pornographic tales. Through five years of engineering, I heard all possible variations of every sex joke.

## Don't Ever Tell Me You Can't

One time, a male classmate pushed a little harder. He approached me and said, "I want to see if you can guess this mysterious sound." He clasped the palms of his hands and pumped them against each other close to my ear, producing a sound that went pffft ... pffft. "What's that?" he asked, and looked at me squarely. "Milking of a cow," I quickly answered. "Wrong," he said, "That's the sound of sexual intercourse." He used a more shocking word. Still a virgin, I was clueless. Sex was an extremely private forbidden matter that parents never talked about to their children. The sound of the whole thing made me feel like I had been violated. I remember looking at his eyes. What I saw was a glimmer of contempt. I looked away but I stayed right where we were.

And stay in the harsh cold world I did. After each semestral break and Christmas vacations, I showed up on the first day of school and every school day thereafter. My action spoke loudly and clearly: I intended to graduate. Soon, the freshman and sophomore years were history, as well as the mental hazing. With my acceptance by the professors and male classmates, life in school became bearable.

Then, an entirely different obstacle emerged. The men, once stern and malicious, now became patronizing. Chivalry threatened to block my path to progress. A unique approach of tact coupled with independence and physical strength solved the problem. It all started in the carpentry class.

In this class, a long table roughened by years of pounding and hacking dominated the shop. Saws, chisels, hammers of steel and wood, and pouches of nails hung on one wall, while finished products adorned the shelves of the other.

"These are the things we will make this semester," said the shop instructor, a small baby-faced man with flattop hair, as he pointed at varnished, carefully constructed cabinets and stuff I had never seen before. He announced projects for the semester: "We will construct "fishplate joints," "mortise and tenon," and "tongue and groove."

The names of the wood joints intimidated me as much as the tools did. They seemed too heavy for me to lift, let alone carry them and push them back and forth. I shuddered at the thought of flunking the carpentry class.

"Your first assignment," he continued, "is to handcraft something like this." He waved a smooth block of wood. "I'll distribute rough pieces of lumber from which you'll start." With that, he dove into a crate and as he called out a name, he yanked out a piece of wood, which a student came forward to get. When my turn came, he handed me an already completed project. A curious smile played about the corner of his mouth when I took it.

Within minutes the giant table became the center of a flurry of activities as the men began measuring, cutting, and chiseling their individual pieces. Their laughter and chatter blended incongruously with the thump and rasp of the tools against the lumber. They were having a blast, while there I sat quietly in one corner, staring at my finished project, wondering what to do with it. I ached to complain to the instructor, to beg him, to let me start from scratch so I could use the hacksaw and chisel, but I did not dare lest he might go to extremes and hand me the power saw and direct me to the rain forest. To keep busy and lighten my frustration, I spent the three-hour class sandpapering my wood block. I kept thinking how unfair the instructor was. He did a disservice to my male classmates and to me. Something needed to be done about it.

When I reached home, all hell in my tortured mind exploded. I ransacked my father's toolbox and took out the hammer, saw, chisel, pencil, folding meter stick. I went for a long piece of lumber. In a hard-driving, almost manic devotion to what I considered just, such as getting my fair share in a difficult facet in engineering school, I squatted on the floor and labored away to produce my very own wood block.

Even though my back hurt, my fingers were bruised, and my shoulders ached from forcing the saw tooth against the grain of the wood back and forth, I was too satisfied to care. I was Noah building his Ark, driven by a deep sense of purpose. I loved the sound of the chisel rasping through the wood, the salt taste of sweat, and the feel of sawdust on my fingers. Best of all, I loved the knowledge that no matter what angle I looked at the wood block, I could proudly say: I made this with my very own two hands.

In the land surveying course, the instructor divided the class into groups. Each group, called a survey crew, consisted of the instrumentman, recorder, front chainman, back chainman, and rodman. The title of the recorder did not have the word "man" attached to it, therefore, in my crew, that was my permanent assignment.

The transitman, our leader, a man who constantly chewed on toothpicks, seemed to delight in seeing me do the recorder's job—sitting on the transit case by him, jotting down numbers he dictated to me, much like a private secretary.

I simply did as I was told, without complaint, like a poodle graduated from obedience school, even when the men were obviously cross-training themselves in the different jobs. One day, before the start of a survey of a government park, I suggested to our leader to let me "handle the gun" or be the instrumentman. He studied my face, mystified why I would even think of wanting his job. "The transit is too heavy for you to set," he answered after spitting out a shredded toothpick. Then he walked away.

The three other men carrying the tripod, rods, pins, hubs and tape followed. Left with no other choices, I simply chased the men. "Can I at least be a rodman?" I hollered in a last-ditch effort to convince our fearless leader to promote me from the recorder's job. "A rodman's job does not demand any talent or special strength."

"No," he yelled back without looking at me. "That takes a lot of walking." He continued to walk.

"But how will I learn?" I asked, as I sped up my pace to keep up with the men's longer strides.

"Not important," the men chorused.

An icy standoff followed. The men moved about their assigned roles. It was just another day of surveying for them.

I started coming to school very early on Saturdays and tinkered with the transit. Every now and then I asked questions to the only other person in the room, the school personnel in charge of the surveying equipment. This went on for a few sessions, until I mastered every screw of the transit.

"Sometimes, you've just got to roll with the punches then swing your own some other way," I would say later, after becoming the first woman to qualify for the age-old land surveyors' examination in New Mexico in 1971.

Coming to school very early to learn the surveying instrument on my own served up a nasty ramification. The equipment man somehow mistakenly surmised that I had been coming early to be alone with him, to seduce him. One evening, perhaps after seeing the light, he followed me to the bus stop. As I was getting off the first jeepney to transfer to another, he grabbed me by the arm and dragged me away from waiting passengers. He wagged his finger at me and angrily said, "You are playing mind games with men." And he ranted about the seduction bit. I shook him loose and I scurried to the first waiting jeepney. It took a while before I figured out who the man was and what he was talking about.

Poverty besieged my parents persistently, but they clung tightly to the same single rope to which I was hanging on—Determination. Father worked longer hours under the baking sun. When he came home at night, the stall was redolent with the vinegary smell of his hard day's sweat. Still, he did not produce enough money. Mother's extra sewing jobs after a hectic day in the market barely dented the family's expenses. She thought of creative ways to increase her sales; she decided to add horsemeat to her inventory. "Fresh beef from Batangas," she told her customers. An otherwise basically honest woman, she so convinced the town folks that one day when she offered genuine beef, no one touched it. They suspected it to be horsemeat.

However, there was always food on the floor at mealtime. Mother cooked everything she failed to sell during the day. They were the grisly meats and the soggiest fish mauled by customers' pinching and checking for freshness. She did not plan for vitamins and minerals. She cooked, and we ate the customers' rejects, period. Sometimes for days on end, she served horsemeat bone soup with swamp greens. She always prepared something to keep our stomachs warm and full.

The problem was tuition fee money that did not come easily. During the week of final examinations, the school registrar published a list of students who were delinquent with their tuition fees. To really grab their attention and embarrass them into meeting their obligations, he posted the list on all conspicuous areas of the campus—on hallways, near stairways, on all sides of the registrar's office.

My name appeared consistently on this "wanted" list, but I always ignored it initially to give my parents a few extra days to scrounge additional money. By the time the grace period expired, they were usually able to pawn some precious possession, like my grandmother's cast iron Dutch oven or big machete. The various loan sharks and pawnshops held deep respect for my parents' determination to see me through college, and for their diligence in paying debts. At an alarming rate lately, my parents were unable to hunt the required tuition fee money, and the professors purged me from the classroom, warning me not to return unless my account was current.

Meanwhile, the educational needs of my brothers and younger sister grew. To cope, Mother budgeted money meticulously. Using empty talcum powder cans as banks, she allocated every centavo to each can labeled "school," "electricity," "rice," "emergency," and others. She doubled as family doctor to save on medical expenses. She boiled herbs and roots and forced us to drink the bitter concoctions for simple diarrhea or constipation. She also practiced a little dentistry. She boiled a certain medicinal bark and insisted we gargle the liquid to strengthen our gums and prevent their bleeding. But in spite of all the efforts, the full force of the heavy hand of poverty eventually snapped my parents' back. They cried for help.

"We can put food on the table and clothes on your back but we can't afford your tuition fees anymore," Father announced, glumly, one suppertime. He walked to the window and stood looking out. "You must find a job, Celia."

My knees buckled under the additional load dumped on my shoulders. Getting a job meant disrupting the routine. I'd have to switch to night school if I were to work during the day or vice versa. I searched my mind for ways to lighten the pressure. What kind of a day job would complement night engineering school? What kind of a night job could I handle after a trying day in engineering school? Location, hours, transportation, type of business, as I weighed them, the task seemed so magnified that I wanted to run away from it. I thought this would be a good excuse to unchain myself from the heavy leg irons of engineering. But then the harrowing events that I had already survived the past two years touched my mind. If I did not find a job, the entire struggle would have been for naught. I could not bear the idea that I had only drained my emotions and convictions to a dark meaningless hole. The thought galvanized me into action.

With qualifications consisting only of one-day work experience in a used-books store and two years of college education, my prospects for a job in a city of two million fiercely competitive people appeared dim. In a society where workplaces held a moral responsibility to employ traditional breadwinners, meaning men, in respect for the family unit, a space for me seemed far-fetched. However, one day I chanced upon a news item about an examination that required a minimum number of college math credits. Anybody who passed it would qualify for a civil service position. I concentrated on this angle of the job-hunting expedition. I threw myself wholeheartedly into the project. I took the government test and passed it. Elation filled my heart when I found out only a handful of candidates among several thousands hurdled the test and that there were also only as many number of jobs available. I was practically guaranteed a government position!

But soon I came face to face with the reality of bureaucracy and the true measure of patience. It took nearly six months and all my patience before I could start working as a surveyor's aide in the Bureau of Lands in a building, which was, fortunately, located only half a mile away from school.

On my first hour of work, I studied the elderly civil servants with whom I'd be working. Like clones, they possessed certain unique characteristics about them. They had expressionless faces worn by years of boredom from doing the same verification of land survey computations submitted by private surveyors. Stripped of ambition by the contentment over a secure job, they moved about without any sense of purpose. Their only excitement consisted of coffee breaks and discussions about future retirement benefits. Somehow, my arrival in their office was a dawning of light. They rejoiced over it. They considered me, the youngest civil servant of that time, an invigorating shot in the arm. They began to train me on the job, without resentment but rather, as a form of amusement in their dull existence.

Thus, my life as a working student unfolded. I was up at the crack of dawn to get ready for work. Then I fought the commuting mob for a space in a jeepney or a bus. Then the day's grind as a surveyor's aide followed. At five o'clock I punched my time card and bolted from the office to jog the half-mile to school. Drenched in sweat from the heat of the setting sun, I arrived panting, and just in time for the first evening class. Then school work occupied me until ten at night. Patiently riding home in heavy, snarled traffic, I usually went to bed close to midnight. The routine was repeated the following day, except on Saturdays and Sundays when school field and laboratory classes filled the daylight hours.

With no more time left for anything else, I set up an arrangement with Mother for handling my finances. After deducting only my allowance for transportation and lunches, I gave her my take-home pay. She shopped for all my needs including slips and shoes and she saved the rest of the money.

In the beginning, it was exciting—the simultaneous challenge of earning money and studying. I reveled at my capabilities. Soon, slowly, my exhilaration in the fast lane wore off. Every fiber of my body seemed to shrink when I slumped to my space on the stall floor near midnight. "What the hell am I doing this for?" I asked myself as I awakened groaning in the small hours of some mornings. But I forced myself right back to sleep, knowing the preciousness of each minute, for another long lonely day must be faced just as surely as the sun will shine.

Frequently, in my fourth year, exhaustion drove me to the limits. At times I seriously considered dropping out of school, but the symbols of my parents' sacrifices would not go away. The sweat that dried into salt on Father's dark neck after a day of toiling under the scorching sun filled the stall with a sour smell. The pig that was being fattened for the next tuition fee stretched lazily near the door. And then there were the pains that had been endured. Everyone's fight had been long and hard already. Instead of quitting, I found myself trying to strengthen the will to continue. And I continued to receive passing school marks, an accomplishment worth a thousand commendations in a school where only twelve out of sixty students went on to graduate from each classroom each semester. Each passing grade evoked a sigh of relief and delight.

My delight over my scholastic achievement, however, could not quite fill the void of something drastically missing in my life, a love life. At age twenty, my heart had not throbbed for a man. I had not dated. When other women students came later and disappeared after marrying an instructor or a classmate, I promised myself not to fall in love with any of the men in engineering school. A few men had been attracted to me over the years but I had stuck to my self-imposed rigid discipline of not getting involved. At age twenty, no man's lips had ever touched mine; no man's hands had caressed my body. I wondered if I was, at all, a normal warm-blooded woman. Would my breasts heave against a man? I had often read about "frigid" and "hot" women. What kind of a woman was I? Was I barren of passion or emotion of any kind? Since I was managing fairly well as a full-time employee and full-time student, I convinced myself there was absolutely nothing wrong with adding to my schedule an extra-curricular activity, like a small affair. I could sandwich a love life between school and office. I talked myself into taking on a boyfriend.

Choosing Ray was not altogether deliberate and cold-blooded. Dashing, athletic, and two years my senior, he had shown special interest in me since high school where his younger sister introduced us. Besides, he seemed to admire qualities in me that other men found disturbing: my independence and fearlessness in defying conventions. He was the only one, outside of my father, to laud my choice of civil engineering. On top of all these, his parents had a catering business that supported his easy living. He drove his own car.

For a couple of months, I sacrificed either school or office time to sneak out with Ray to the movies and to the seashore. When for the first time he put his arms around me, our closeness made me gasp. Kissing with my eyes closed, I thrilled at the discovery of myself as a woman, perfectly capable of feeling and reciprocating the touch of a man.

This discovery proved to be my undoing. Full-time employment, full-time schooling, and steady necking were too much of a demand. Schoolwork showed a damning evidence of my shattered concentration. My grades plummeted. I flunked all but English and Philosophy.

Father's eyes narrowed when he saw my report card. He paced the floor of the stall, speechless with rage, clutching his chest. When he regained his composure, he droned, "I don't know. Perhaps I'm destined to die without seeing a child of mine become an engineer." He popped two asthma pills in his mouth and gulped a glass of water. He slumped in one corner of the room, frowning darkly. The world seemed to close in on him, hopelessly.

It might as well have been an impassioned plea. I stared at him, unseeing, from where I sat on the floor diagonally across him. Although remorseless over my reckless adventure, and still hot from dawdling towards the fire of passion, I knew I had gone far enough without scorching my skin. It was time to pull back. Something had to make room here and now: school, job, or lover. Lover was bumped out in the reorganization of priorities.

As easily as I had steered myself into an affair, I veered out of it without difficulty. It was nothing but a habit that needed to be curbed. Before the start of the following semester, Ray had become just a memory. Although I was sure my romantic involvement had been nothing concrete or colossal, I knew Ray had been more serious. He had proposed marriage. For that reason, for a while, I felt guilty. But soon, even this

41

feeling faded away. I plowed into the books with the determination of a donkey to make up for lost time.

In 1964, the year I had envisioned, I finally marched on stage accompanied by the recorded song of Roy Hamilton's "Walk On" to claim my diploma in civil engineering. *"When you walk through the storm hold your head up high and don't be afraid of the dark..."* The lyrics of the song sent goosebumps all over my body. As I shook hands with well-wishers who had waited for me at the foot of the stage, I was flushed with victory. I floated on exquisite heights of joy. Wallowing in the bliss of naiveté, I did not know my hard-earned diploma, that little piece of paper which Father and I had so doggedly pursued, was just the wick of explosive combats to come.

# Chapter 6

# A Man's World, Part I

inally, Mother hoarded enough money from my earnings, that of Father's, and hers to build a conventional house away from the public market. It was a basic dwelling, two-story to make the best out of a compact lot, with two small bedrooms on the upper level. A combined kitchen and dining room, which also doubled as a bedroom, filled the lower level. The house featured a lifetime dream of mine: a toilet and bathroom! Water dripped only at night when community demand was low, therefore, Father and my brothers rotated in staying up all night to collect the precious commodity in various tin containers for use the following day in the kitchen and the bathroom.

I will always remember the day I entered the bathroom for the first time.

Shutting the door behind me for that long-coveted privacy, I braced myself for a moment of revelry. I dipped my hand in a bucket and allowed the sensation from the cold water to travel to every tissue of my whole body. Then I ran my fingertips around the rim of the white ceramic bowl-shaped fixture. Stepping back slightly, I admired its majestic construction. Built directly atop a mightily reinforced septic tank, its base was clamped tightly to the rough concrete floor. Its strategic height extended a tempting invitation. Surrendering to the commode's persuasive call for action, I went ahead and tested its viability. With mission accomplished, I poured a bucketful of water and savored the rapturous moment when for the very first time in my life, I saw our very own toilet bowl gurgle. Wallowing in high luxurious living with this indoor bathroom, I couldn't help but pat my back for helping make it happen. I marched out of the room, grinning, The era of hiding behind the bushes and under the goblin's sheet had, at long last, ended.

## Celia Ruiz-Tomlinson

I had never seen Mother as splendidly happy as she was on the day she moved into this house. She gazed dreamily at the plywood ceiling, at the roughly finished masonry wall, and at the wooden floor. She opened and shut the louvered windows. She switched the fluorescent lights on and off. "This," she proudly announced, "is privacy. This is permanence." The house embodied her dream of a place where the women of the family could undress without fear of being watched by drunks lurking behind the market tables. The house also represented freedom from constant fear of being evicted from the public land where we had been squatters. It was also absolute proof of her talent as a magician in stretching the peso to make both ends meet and save some, for it took immense amount of money to build this basic house.

Immediately, she set out to sew curtains of colorful cotton materials. She hung family pictures on the wall. As special tribute to my accomplishment, she gave my college graduation portrait, the one with the Mona Lisa smile, a prominent space directly opposite the entry door. She made sure it greeted anyone setting foot in the house. She was happy, I was happy.

My happiness over my graduation paled against Father's euphoria. He took leave from work for a special trip to his hometown which he had not visited leisurely in twelve years. He had made a few escorted trips only to testify in the murder case, and now, the culprits languished in prison. He had no more fears. Father made the round of his relatives and in between bites of sticky sweet rice cakes, bragged about his daughter, *the civil engineer.* He had reached his goal.

But graduation was only the beginning for me. The end of the tunnel couldn't be seen yet; the long road stretched ahead. I must pass the national examinations for civil engineers.

To prepare for the examinations, I took two months from work just to study, study, and study. Up by the first crow of the neighbor's rooster at the break of dawn, I solved problems on borrowed books, honing up on my slide rule at every opportunity. For practical experience, I tried to get a job with a construction company, but was refused. However, nothing prevented me from pressing my nose against chainlink fences, looking in from the outside of job sites. I watched men build forms, bend bars, and pour concrete. I watched Father hammer away at planks. When a building was being constructed across from my office, I spent my breaks watching men measure, saw, chisel, cut, and pour.

Examination day came and six months later the list of names of successful examinees was published in the front page of Manila's dailies. My name was not included in the list. I flunked in a most miserable way. My top scores in surveying, hydraulics, and mathematics simply could not offset my low grade in construction.

44

The news of my failure was a double-edged sword that stabbed my heart. The low grade in construction only screamed the need for more exposure to construction methods. How, oh, how could I get it if no building or road contractors wanted to hire me? The prospect of seeing the light at the end of the tunnel dimmed.

My failure was sensed and mourned beyond the limits of my supportive family. You'd think a coffin had dropped through a hole on the ceiling. A coffin with the family dream in it. There was emptiness from wall to wall of the house.

But not for long. Father led the revival march of the wounded. And everyone agreed that the dream was not dead; it was just on hold. There was no room to spew over our misfortune, only for positive thinking. It was true and easy for them to say but the heavy hand of pressure pounded my back again. I could hardly wait to rise from the ruins to vindicate myself and to get everyone's expectation off me.

Following a year of more intensive review, study, and observation which, this time, included regular visits to job sites of former classmates who were by now running around as project engineers, I subjected myself once more to the grueling task of formal testing. When I turned in my examination book at the end of the last day of testing, I felt a rumble in the pit of my stomach hit the rock bottom of helplessness. The matter was now out of my hands. Mentally exhausted, I searched my conscience if I had done everything I could. The pressure of wanting to pass the tests this time weighed on me heavily. I wanted to cry but couldn't.

Waiting for the examination results this time around was torture. I must have talked to all the engineers who had flunked on their first attempt and passed on their second try, hoping to extract from them even an ounce of hope and encouragement. A majority of them suggested that I do what they did: offer devotion every Thursday night to Saint Jude, the patron saint of hopeless causes. I admired their faith, but deep within me, I believed my case was not right up the good saint's alley. There were times when I lay awake in the middle of the night deliberating the direction of my fate should I flunk again. These were the moments when I found myself overwhelmed, and with no place to turn to, groaning words like "Please make me pass!" to the Higher Power.

Six months passed and one morning my eyes connected with an item on the front page about the civil engineering national examination results. Immediately, my heart pounded against my chest. My life hung on this one important press issue. All my apprehension dissipated when I found my name among the one hundred ninety two—out of five hundred and six examinees—who had passed!

## Celia Ruiz-Tomlinson

It was one day of unforgettable excitement. Pure unadulterated bliss! I felt warm all over, all day, drugged with the delight over the submergence of dream and reality. Everything I looked at seemed magnified in beauty and substance. The name Celia Ruiz leaped from the pages of the newspapers then soared on to a theater marquee, crazy neon lights flashing about it. When I ate at mealtime, I gazed about rapturously, as though I was partaking of an intoxicating bacchanalian feast. That night, it seemed like I slept floating five feet above my bed, with my eyes wide open.

In 1966, the Philippine Board of Examiners for Civil Engineers registered me, Celia Suva Ruiz, Civil Engineer Number 7704.

When the certificate arrived, Father was ecstatic. He talked about it shamelessly. The neighbors thought he was the one who had pinned down the registration. He took another bragging trip to his hometown to herald the magnificent news about his daughter, the *registered* civil engineer.

Upon his return to the city, he demolished the front part of our house. Wood planks and nails screeched as he pried them apart with a crowbar. He unscrewed the louvered windows from the upstairs sills, sending them crashing to the concrete pad in front of the house.

Jolted by the noise, Mother careened from the back where she had been hanging clothes on the outdoor line. When she saw the small wreckage, her first thought was that Father's mind had come unhinged. "Whatever possessed you to tear down our house?" Mother exploded at him, her chin shaking with anger. In her hands was a dripping bed sheet she had been washing.

Father, leaning against the crowbar, remained cool and collected. Studying the messed-up front of the house, he gave the reason behind his premeditated demolition. "We will build a house at this same place. It will be one of poured structural concrete, a house with an overhanging balcony, Spanish style. It will be Celia's first project. So you see, when our neighbors pass by, they'll notice the construction and they'll be curious. They will ask "Who designed your house?' and I'll say, "My daughter, the engineer. Isn't that a wild scheme?"

He added that people needed to know the availability of a competent civil engineer in the neighborhood; someone whom they knew. Such was his idea of successful promotions.

Mother shrugged hopelessly. By now, the intensity of her shock over things engineering had decreased. However, she still could not understand such a blithe disrespect for the product of her years of saving, but what could she do? The important thing to her now was to get the house rebuilt and repossess the family's privacy!

Father drew a rough sketch of the proposed house. Same two levels, same layout as before except that this time around the outside walls would be poured concrete, not masonry blocks. And of course, the overhanging balcony.

"Now, design the cantilevered balcony," he said, handing the drawing to me. There was a hint of dare in his voice.

Fresh from the board exams, I took on Father's order with confidence. I really had no choice. The house must be reconstructed immediately. Every night for a week, I came home directly from work to design Father's grandiose plans. After drawing lines, computing, measuring, and cranking my slide rule, I came up with my recommendation.

"Here you are," I announced proudly, "five-inch thick slab, number five steel reinforcement, eight-inch thick walls."

"Very well," Father acknowledged. He took the paper, field it as far away from his face as he could, and squinted his eyes to see well. "We will start building."

No sooner said than done. In the days that followed, Father and my two teenaged brothers hammered and trowelled away. They mixed concrete in a pit on the ground, using shovels. They wheelbarrowed the mixture and poured it laboriously into forms. Meanwhile, the whole family lived in the middle of the mess—piles of lumber, bags of cement, a stack of paint cans, mounds of nails, pails of water, a ladder, and other pieces of evidence of work in progress.

Every time I came home, I inspected the project curiously, measuring forms, checking pieces of lumber, and the steel bars. And then I noticed a few deviations from my design. The slab was seven inches, not five; the steel bars were number seven also, not five. Hacked off by the obvious disregard for my design, I confronted Father.

"Why did you increase every figure I gave you?" I asked.

"I have to play it safe," he said, bemusedly. "I used a factor of two— one for factor of safety, and one for ignorance. I don't trust new engineers, especially a woman engineer."

My problems in the men's world of engineering had obviously just surfaced. It was incredible; my own father, who had supported me all along, both morally and financially, had issued such a statement. What would it be like with the other men?

Father's construction skills and my engineering knowledge combined as snugly as a mortise-and-tenon wood joint. After the last coat of paint was applied to the exterior of the house, Father and I stepped back a hundred meters to analyze our project from afar, just in case we had been too close to it. When the final long-distance inspection was over, the smiles on our faces declared the house reconstruction a resounding triumph.

The structure rivaled the pyramids of Egypt in strength. Father's factors of safety and ignorance, in addition to those of mine, yielded a mini-building massive with the mixture of concrete and steel. It stood proudly, unafraid of future raging monsoon rains and intensity six earthquakes.

The success of the project emboldened Father and me to try our hands at other construction ventures, at small-time contracting. We submitted a bid to build the local elementary school flagpole, and we won over five others who coveted the job. Father and I tackled the project with characteristic gusto, but always with the friction typical to the grating of a construction man's practical idea against a college graduate's learned theory. We argued about the size of the flagpole base.

"But why do you make it so massive?" I asked.

"Because I know more about construction than you do," he announced. "Besides I don't trust a woman engineer."

It was the final insult I would take from my mentor. After the inauguration of the flagpole, I decided to take the plunge into the engineering arena immediately, to gain outside experience and credibility. I put in applications for jobs with construction companies and engineering consulting firms. Not one soul honored me with a response. The government departments that had anything to do with engineering came next on my list: Public Works, Highways, and National Development. They did not want me, either; they preferred men. Would I like, they were curious, to be a draftsman like other women engineers? I refused gracefully.

I scanned the classified ads religiously. In the '60s they were segregated into Female Help Wanted and Male Help Wanted columns. Plumbers, electricians, and all building trades belonged exclusively under the Male category. So did the engineers. Secretaries, nurses, schoolteachers, and seamstresses belonged under the Female department. A civil engineer under it was extremely unlikely but I kept looking at the classified ads without fail, rain or shine. I responded to some of the engineer wanted ads under the Male column, but was totally ignored. One time, just to grab the personnel manager's attention, I attached to my résumé a picture of myself dressed in figure-revealing black leotards, and posed leaning against a neighbor's motorcycle. I enclosed a self-addressed stamped envelope for his reply. Neither the photograph nor a reply came back.

After three frustrating months, my spirits began to sag. I wondered a hundred times why I had struggled so hard, and so long to become a registered civil engineer when no one would probably give me a chance to practice my profession. Everything had been in vain, I thought. Maybe it's time to give up, to move on to more realistic things.

Well, not quite yet, my fighting spirit protested. Each morning always brought a flicker of hope within me. I continued checking out the classified ads in search of a miracle. One Sunday, a miracle did happen: a Help Wanted Lady Engineer appeared!

What an awesome ad it was! My eyeballs nearly popped out of their sockets at the sight of this ad. I blinked repeatedly in disbelief and moved the newspaper at various distances and angles from my face. When finally convinced the ad was for real, I darted to the kitchen where Mother was plucking feathers off a dead chicken.

"This is for me. Look!" I shouted joyously, jumping up and down, waving the newspaper in front of her face.

"Take it easy," Mother said, coolly. "Don't get too excited." But when she found out my news meant the possibility of leaving my government job, color drained out of her face. "You have a secure job. It cost you blood and sweat to get it. Now you will leave it just like that." She was almost pleading.

Mother's misgivings dampened my enthusiasm some, but not enough to change my mind. Even though she discoursed at length about the family's long history of financial hardships, my resolve to get out in the engineering world became stronger.

"I must take the chance. I've got to work as an engineer sometime between ages twenty three and sixty five." I said with finality.

Mother went on trying to persuade me to stay with the government. She talked about retirement and pension and being fixed in my old age but to no avail. My mind had already been set to answer the ad, which read: WANTED LADY ENGINEER. APPLY IN PERSON. H. R. LOPEZ & CO. QUEZON CITY. And I did.

Why suddenly that ad? As I brushed my long hair, a stream of thoughts ran through my mind. Inevitably, doors had opened for me in the past for things I wanted. The high school math contest. I was only an alternate, and yet at the last minute, a special event was created and I emerged a winner. The press conference. I was not selected delegate, and yet at the last minute, the adviser chose me to replace an official representative who suddenly became ill, and I went on to win a medal. One common factor stood out. When the door screeched open, I was at the doorstep, ready to seize the opportunity when it presented itself. Could a door be opening for me now, with that ad? But why a lady engineer? After checking my face one last time, I picked up my purse and set out to find the answers at the second interview.

It took two bus transfers to get to the H. R. Lopez compound, an impressive spread of land outside Manila occupied by an office and a yard of several orange-painted heavy equipment. In the office, a trim, bespectacled, young engineer motioned for me to sit down in front of his large mahogany desk. Without preliminary, he told me I beat out two other applicants.

"You were better qualified than them," he said, shuffling

applications in a manila folder. He focused his eyes on a slightly older Chinese-looking engineer in another desk and introduced him.

"Sexier, too," added the Chinese-looking engineer, smiling. His doe eyes moved up and down my figure appreciatively.

"That's why I voted to hire you."

A smile dawned on my lips, too. I marveled at how a thought of lechery might have pushed the older man's decision. Or did it? Sexier. The word flattered me, undoubtedly, although I never saw my competitors in the man's private sensuality contest. A woman, by nature, possesses something capable of softening a man's heart. Sexy. I had thought that, too, of me in the picture I had attached to one résumé. That ought to call the personnel manager's attention, I said, but I never heard a squeak from the man. When it came right down to business in this inhospitable engineering world, sexy did not really mean a thing. No, they selected me because I was already a registered engineer, I convinced myself.

H. R. Lopez & Co., one of the largest earthmoving firms in the Philippines, had operations that stretched all the way to the southern islands.

Knowing this, I carried a vision with me all the way home. I could see myself quite clearly wearing khaki coveralls and a bright yellow hard hat, a rolled set of plans tucked under my arm, and scurrying about construction sites from one island to the other. My imagination went wild at home. "Engineer Celia Ruiz," I said, aloud, grinning broadly in front of the bathroom mirror, thinking how weird my name sounded with the title, but how heavenly the prospect was.

On my first day of work, H. R. Lopez, the pudgy, cigar-chomping owner of the company changed my whole vision. He dropped the bombshell as to why he hired a lady engineer. "I want someone in the engineering room to answer the phone and file paperwork and catalogs," he said, pointing to a chaotic stack of letters and colorful brochures of International Harvester, Bucyrus Erie, and Allis Chalmers. "In other words, you studied engineering, you will know what you are filing."

The blow was so hard it took a while for me to recover. I fell apart inside, like I wanted to cry but couldn't. Momentarily, the thought occurred to me that this company of men had cheated me. Had they told me during the first interview about my filing duties, I might have refused the honor of being the lady engineer of the company. On top of this humiliation, they were going to pay me less than my government salary. I kept thinking it wasn't too late to turn back, and I weighed the options available to me. I could retrieve my job and my snug little corner of the world, then wait for another miracle to happen under the Female Help Wanted column. Or, I could stay and work at adjusting the attitudes at H. R. Lopez & Co.

I was learning an important lesson to let the past go clearly, to sacrifice it to make room for an expanding future. I numbly opted to stay.

For days, I shuffled Allis Chalmers catalogs, many times staring at them murderously, and many times toying with the idea of tossing them in the nearest trash can. One morning, I thought I might just make a lemonade out of this lemon job that I got. I pored through the reading material, really digesting every written word, and to my surprise, the brochures introduced me to a world I might otherwise have never known. That Allis Chalmer HD-21 for example, was a heavy-duty hunk of a machine that could plow into a mountain of dirt without shaking. There are other eye openers: loaders, graders, tractors, sheepsfoot rollers—their looks, their functions, and their horrendous costs. When the phone rang, I always answered it promptly. "Engineering," I'd say, my voice one octave higher than normal, just like secretaries did, just in case H. R. was checking out my style.

The charade slowly took its toll. At the end of my third month on the job, my optimism plunged to an all-time low. Like a fierce bull tied to a tree, I yearned to charge into the open wild of engineering where engineers did what engineers were supposed to be doing.

One day, the right climate seemed to be set for the move to make the two male engineers share their technical work with me. Several rolls of blueprints and specification books cluttered their desks. More work material overflowed to the adjoining drafting boards. My brochures were in a neat little pile against the wall; my desktop clean and clear. It was my moment just waiting to happen. I swiveled my chair to face Billy, the younger engineer. There he was, a study in concentration, writing little figures on a chart.

"Billy," I said, rolling my chair closer to him. Do you remember my college transcript of records during the interview? I was really great in surveying and earthwork. May I help you with some of your work?"

"I don't need help," Billy grumped, pushing his rimless glasses up his nose. His voice was flat, vehement and uncompromising.

"Yes, you do. Look at all that work piled up on your desk," I prodded. "Are you afraid I might do it so well you might lose your job?"

Ego. That was something about the machos that I found vulnerable.

Larry, the older engineer, roared with laughter, throwing his chin up in the air. "She thinks school and actual practice are the same. Go ahead. Give her a take-off job. See if she can do it."

"Why not," he said. He reached for a set of plans. "Here, do the site preparation and surfacing take-off."

Site preparation and surfacing take-off! So engineering. The words rang in my head. Plan in hand, I rolled back to my desk. A sense of excitement warmed my heart. It was, after all, my first *really* engineering work outside of Father's domain.

Upon spreading the plans on the table, I began to flip the blueprints aimlessly. Questions flooded my mind. Like what do I do? Where do I start? Where do I end? What is normally done? What is expected of me? But asking the men would mean cowardly surrender. The men were right; school and practice were not the same.

I stared at the drawings and concentrate on the lines that were trying to say something. Then, slowly, the muster of lines cleared up. It was like going to a pitch dark movie house where after several minutes, the pupils adjust to the darkness, then soon people's heads begin to form. Likewise, the plans came to life. The curb and gutter, sidewalks, underground pipes, and drainage ditch seemed to leap from the drawings. My hands switched from the engineer's scale to the slide rule to the calculator to the estimate form. I was on my way to completing my first quantity take-off. Armed with total confidence, I proudly presented the tabulation to the men.

Billy gave the estimate sheet a critical eye while I held my breath, waiting for his verdict. He compared the figures with what he had on another sheet. He kept nodding his head. After a few minutes, he said, "Do this other set of plans, too." He laid the drawings on my desk.

Billy's voice was, all of a sudden, music to my ears.

In the days that followed, I tiptoed away from the catalogs. By the time H. R. noticed them piled high again, he could no longer ignore my value as an engineer. In fact, he raised my pay. When he did, I pushed a little harder, and suggested he assign me as field engineer.

"Don't be ridiculous," he answered in a voice that fell as final as an axe. "That job is for men." He abandoned my conversation and strutted out of the room, leaving me nothing but a billow of stinky cigar smoke and a threat of a lifetime of armchair engineering.

# Chapter 7

❧❧

# A Man's World, Part 2

Upon receiving my license to practice as a civil engineer, I joined the Philippine Association of Civil Engineers. In 1966, I was the first and only female engineer, and the youngest member of the respected association. As I recall, none of my classmates, male or female joined. Looking back now, I realize why. The simple activity of attending a meeting tested one's endurance.

From the main highway outside Manila, the dirt road snaked around trees up a hill, leading to all old building that housed the Philippine Association of Civil Engineers. It was quite a hike, this rendezvous of the elite graying engineers already established in the business, but for someone like me who did not have a car, it was the only way. Beating this path on my high-heeled shoes usually sapped my strength, but it never stopped me from attending the meetings once a month. I had to. I was making a statement: If it has anything to do with engineering, I'm there.

The first time I entered the room the men stared at me as someone not worthy of admittance into the bosom of the society of the brotherhood. To gain acceptance, I attempted to strike a conversation with anyone whose eyes were glazed with boredom, or happened to lock with mine. But my efforts fell flat. The men's indifference eventually shoved me to one corner, barred from active participation, and I kept struggling to stay awake during the long drawn-out, boring sessions. As miserable as I was, it never occurred to me to drop out of the exclusive club. I possessed all the requirements for membership and, by golly, *I belonged, whether they liked it or not.* I was not about to give the old goats the satisfaction of seeing me quit.

One day I received a ticket for the association's annual Engineers' Night. For the first time, the president bent over backwards to make sure I would not miss the affair. He even shocked me with a follow-up phone call at work. I wanted to freeze that moment of self-importance. I asked him what the affair was about, hoping to drag on the conversation.

"The Engineers' Night is a fundraising event. It's the only affair of the year that we hold at night. Will you attend?" he asked, his voice with a smile I could hear.

"Certainly," I said, amused by the silly question. "I have attended every meeting. Why would I skip this one?"

"Just wanted to be sure," he said. "See you there, then," he said. The phone receiver clicked on its cradle.

The thoughtfulness of the president, a bleak man of about sixty-five, left me totally mystified.

Mother sewed a knee-length cherry red dress for me to wear at the Engineers' Night. Ruffles of the soft material highlighted the v-neckline of the sleeveless outfit. When I tried it on, her critical eyes were my mirrors. When she said it needed to be taken in a little at the waist, I peeled the dress from my body and she patiently worked on it again. When I tried it on again, she was pleased, I was pleased.

The date came. I put on my new dress, with Mother hovering around me, zipping me up and making sure the ruffles hung evenly. After wearing my freshly shined shoes, I turned around for Mother's final inspection. She nodded her approval. Everything looked great.

"Your brother will accompany you," she declared unequivocally.

I frowned. I had never liked that custom of a brother escorting his sister at her affair, unless it was her choice.

"Mother, this is for engineers only," I said. I reached for my black clutch purse. "He will be out of place there."

Mother, who had not been exactly a shrinking violet in her youth, might have agreed with me but her protectiveness prevailed. "It's night time. If this party was held during the day, I'd let you go by yourself." She paused for a moment to see if I'd argue. When she heard no response but saw my eyebrows knit, she continued. "It's your father who wants your brother to accompany you." It was an easy way out for her. She had raised us to think Father's word was final.

To avoid a family feud, I agreed. I told Rodolfo to wear his Sunday best and call a cab. Under the watchful eyes of our parents, we got in the back seat together. I gave the driver instructions and off we went. When the cab was several blocks away from the house, I asked the driver to pull up at the side of the street to let off my brother. Rodolfo dutifully took another cab and went someplace else.

Unbelieving looks swept over the engineers' faces when they

saw me enter the door, unescorted, an unthinkable act for a Filipino woman at the time. They couldn't have matched my disbelief. For a long time, I studied the crowd, wondering where the men's wives or girlfriends were. Only men milled about except for less than half a dozen waitresses who sashayed in and out of the masses. Nowhere to my recollection, did the ticket or the president say the Engineers' Night was a stag party. But perhaps, the affair was intended exclusively for engineers, the same reason I had banished my brother. Before I could even begin to figure out what was going on, brightness filled the hall and a slender man with thin hair and hollowed eyes, sauntered to the dead center of the floor. A dozen women of my age, with pretty faces thick with rouge and fake eyelashes joined and flanked him. They wore flowing gowns and veils as though they were bridesmaids from various weddings.

"These ladies will take turns performing and passing the hat around for our annual fundraising," the man announced over the microphone. "Sit back, enjoy yourselves, and please be as generous as you can. We want to make enough money to boost our scholarship fund."

Nearly all the country's engineers came out of the woods to attend the association's night of nights. They were there, snazzy, tipsy, outdoing one another with bawdy stories, and rating the charms of the cocktail waitresses who plied the dimly-lit hall, balancing trays of drinks on their shoulders.

A new question popped in my head. Where was this association's scholarship fund when I needed it? It could have definitely eased my parents' financial burden. The association had done a good job keeping the fund a secret, or had it set aside strictly for boys.

The men headed for chairs that had been arranged in circular fashion, leaving plenty of room at the center of the hall. Baldheaded fat men flanked me. The live band conductor, slinky in his black fringed outfit, raised his hand with the baton. The musicians, uniformed in red, focused their eyes on him in unison, their instruments cocked to produce the first musical note at his command.

Soon, an incredible show unfolded before me. The teasing tune from the band began throbbing. One woman slithered rhythmically to the dance floor while the others hid behind a drape at one end of the room. As she swung and swayed her hips, she removed the veil, then the ribbon from her head, allowing her long shiny black hair to fall. She picked the straw hat of the oldest engineer in the room, then as seductively as her sexy eyes could possibly look, she gyrated her smooth belly about six inches from the man's wrinkled face. The man pulled a ten-peso bill from his shirt pocket and tossed it into the hat. The woman removed her flimsy shawl and hugged the donor who in turn suggestively spread his legs.

Boisterous laughter and wild shouts acknowledged the opening act.

The woman swayed on to the next man, who dropped a twenty-peso bill into the hat. She removed the top of her gown, exposing firm brown breasts, and continued to bounce them with the swinging of her full rounded hips.

I gasped in horror. The men cheered and turned their faces to my direction. Their eyes bore into me, undressing me. Written all over their faces were the words, "Now show us you're one of us."

I quickly avoided their eyes and focused my stare on the stripteaser, who continued to bump and grind to the next engineer, a crushed-looking businessman nattily attired in a pinstriped suit. He dangled a fifty-peso bill in front of the woman's eyes, then inserted it between her skirt and waist. She plucked the folded bill, threw it into the hat, unhooked her skirt which immediately fell to the waxed wooden floor. She undulated her naked body in erotic gyrations.

The aroused men roared like a bunch of wild apes, then turned to me again with that dare in their eyes.

The dancer's exposed body, pubic hair and all, jiggling in wild abandon, so shocked me that I had to fight an almost overpowering temptation to flee. I tried with all my might to keep a straight face, to bear the scenario with unruffled equanimity, to deny the men the pleasure of seeing me embarrassed. My lips tightened and a spastic paralysis gripped the muscles around my cheekbones. Soon, a breath of air passed through my parched lips and my muscles loosened up. My eyes held a steady gaze. It was a defining moment. It marked the beginning of the training of my face not to commit to any emotion but blankness. The poker face I so courageously worked on helped me achieve my objective. The men's curiosity about me dissipated before the first stripper completed her number. They left me alone, whole and intact, and concentrated on the girlie show.

While the second stripper geared up to slink on center stage, I stood up awash with a quaint sense of triumph. I bade goodbye cheerfully to those next to me. I donated five pesos, and told the president I'd be glad to get involved in another kind of fundraising. I told the men that naked women just did not do anything for me.

I learned later that I had left an indelible mark in the social annals of Philippine civil engineering. That night became the Philippine Association of Civil Engineers' last Engineers' Night. Impacted by my presence, the organization ended the tradition, resorting instead to tamer fundraising activities such as raffles and pancake breakfasts. As a matter of fact, the president asked me to chair the committee in charge of soliciting prizes for the next community involvement affair.

## Don't Ever Tell Me You Can't

ฺ๛ฺ๛ฺ๛ฺ๛

In the mid-'60s, the war between North and South Viet Nam escalated. The American involvement became evident in the Philippines when the Officer in Charge of Construction (OICC, a section of the U.S. Navy) let out contracts, at a furious rate, for the design and construction of military support facilities in Southeast Asia.

The fashionable business row of Makati bulged with engineering consulting firms like Amman & Whitney, Adrian Wilson & Associates, and Frank L. Hope & Associates. World-class contractors such as Vinnell Corporation, Hood Corporation, E. E. Black, and Morrison-Knudsen moved in for the construction phase. American suppliers claimed their slice of the pie; the likes of Connell Bros., Getz Bros., and Ingraham came to sell their wares. The newspapers burst with full-page ads competing for the attention of architects, engineers, draftsmen, tradesmen, salesmen, and clerical help. Even janitors were in demand. Ironically, while blood spilled on one corner of the Pacific Ocean, economy boomed on another.

Meanwhile, at H. R. Lopez & Co. my enthusiasm waned. The attitudes of the two office engineers had been adjusted, but H. R. remained adamant whenever I asked for a field assignment. He came close though to a compromise when he gave me the site preparation job for Saint Joseph Hospital.

"But the project is just behind our building," I protested while I craned my neck to look through the window.

"Exactly. I don't want you out there. Field engineers are men," he said irrevocably. With that, he walked towards the door, leaving me again with nothing but a rolling mass of smelly smoke.

I took his statement to simply mean field engineers were not women at H. R. Lopez & Co. The irresistible call of the wild engineering jungle hounded me once more. I quit my job to continue the search for my rightful place under the sun.

Adrian Wilson & Associates hired me in its civil department. A big company of hundreds of employees, its pecking order reduced me to one of the lesser technical humans, the draftsmen and lower technicians. The male Americans held the prime choice positions while the male Filipino engineers had the second best jobs.

I regretted the move the instant I saw the sea of faces behind drafting tables. Suddenly, I was nothing but one employee among many. Feeling insignificant in a crowd of engineers and architects on a floor of a high-rise building, I missed the quiet and intimate atmosphere of a small congenial office. I considered going back to H. R. Lopez to plead to him to take me back. But I steeled myself against the temptation and decided to give it a little time to make it work out. I took the opportunity to learn everything that the estimating department had to offer.

As if the lowly treatment did not suffice, the American office manager at one time issued a memorandum to the effect that all Filipinos must address each American engineer as "sir." The memorandum disgusted me about the place even more, but I quickly thought of a creative way to handle the situation. On the way to cash our paychecks, I suggested, and everybody unanimously seconded, that we call each and every live human being a "sir" regardless of age, color, sex, race, or country of origin. No distinctions allowed. Even the old woman who came every morning to sell fried banana snacks to the employees became a "sir." Thus, everybody at Adrian Wilson & Associates enjoyed equality.

The office manager ripped the memorandum off the bulletin board immediately.

Humoring equality did not cure my frustrations. My pay, which was good by Philippine standard, did not satisfy me. Competitiveness kept nagging me to break out of the suffocating mediocrity; to get an engineering job that would jump-start my spirits and wire my senses to a state of high alert. When I could no longer contain my restlessness, I set out to find me another job.

"Again?" Mother's voice thundered when she heard my renewed search for employment. "Why can't you be satisfied with anything? What do you want?"

"Another job." I replied.

Mother's love for immediate hard cash grated against my determined effort to establish myself as a respectable civil engineer. A fierce argument erupted between us, but Father came to my rescue, as usual, when it came to furthering my career.

Atlantica Corporation hired me as its company engineer and occasional sales representative. The Asian contact of an American company, and fully owned and controlled by a Chinese family, Atlantica supplied imported construction materials to the local OICC contractors. It did brisk business under the "Buy American" policy of the OICC whereby all building materials for the support facilities must originate from the United States of America, with reasonable exceptions like gravel, sand, and lumber. Otherwise, even nails must be shipped from America.

The new job offered me a different kind of stimulation. Working with Chinese businessmen and Filipino secretaries and clerks, I soaked in the glory of being the only engineer in the company. I was special; I had expertise and background nobody else had, not even John Lim, the handsome, company president whose business acumen secretly impressed me. From what I gathered, he had built up this business empire through the sweat of his brow from poverty. The job also gave me a ringside view of the profitable operations of a businessman in the fringes of the engineering arena.

As the company engineer, I studied all the OICC plans to take note of importable profitable construction materials and their specifications. We offered substitutions when necessary to make more money, and I worked out the details with the OICC engineer. When Atlantica bid to supply huge amounts of aluminum or steel, I reviewed and signed the proposal and affixed my engineer's seal where required. As an occasional sales representative, I kept Atlantica abreast of the needs of various American agencies that related to construction. In short, mine was a sales, technical, and glamour job.

In this job, I encountered an entirely new batch of frustrations. The buyers, who were all men, saw me only as a sweet young thing marketing herself for the ultimate goal of marriage. I tried to explain my job but no one cared to listen. No one took me seriously. Instead of asking technical questions about the products Atlantica was offering, they asked if I wanted to go dancing or to celebrate New Year's Eve with them. I focused my attention on the salesmen, hoping to learn what made them click with the buyers, only to find out they played the game of lavishing the buyers with wine, women, and song. I gave the formula a try but when one buyer took on my invitation for a seafood dinner to talk to him about tiles or aluminum roll-up doors, it turned out he had something else entirely in mind.

My most memorable challenge in the engineering sales field happened on my very first visit to the U.S. Air Force Procurement Office. There I met a John Begandy, a dishwaterblond master sergeant who headed the crew of buyers. John struck a conversation that ranged from typhoons to ice cream, and jeepneys, completely ignoring the fact that I had gone to his office to drum up some business. When he stopped to take a breath, I attempted to detour his attention to my purpose. I handed him my business card.

"I just want to further introduce myself." I smiled.

John's face expressed some disgust as he read the card—"Celia S. Ruiz, Civil Engineer, Sales Representative, Atlantica Corporation." A dramatic change came over him afterwards. He tossed my card into a trashcan. "Don't give me any of those damned cards," he said, abruptly. He looked at me squarely, taking note of my reaction.

My mouth fell, but I quickly smiled at John to camouflage my shock. I stood up. "I have two hundred of those cards," I said, calmly. "I'll see you again sometime and give you another one." With that I walked out of his office.

One week later, I returned to submit a proposal to supply 200,000 square feet of aluminum sheets. I caught him in a jovial mood, humming a bouncy tune, his head bobbing to it, as he shuffled purchase order.

"Good morning!" I said, happily, encouraged by his hint of a bright disposition.

"Mornin'!" He interrupted his humming, looked up, and smiled at me. He motioned me to sit down, that I did, and I handed him Atlantica's bid in a sealed manila envelope, which he cheerfully accepted.

He engaged me in small talk for a few minutes, then all of a sudden, he held my hand. "Sweetie, do you dance?" He was smiling.

"Yes, I do," I replied, brushing away his hand very tactfully. "Do you?"

"Nope, I don't care for that."

"What do you care for?"

"Nothing. I don't care for nothing, I don't need nothing." He acted angry.

He started moving things around, the telephone, a paperweight, the files, ignoring my presence.

I could not tell if he was trying to be funny, difficult, or proud, so I stood up. "Oh well," I finally gasped in exasperation. "Excuse me, I forgot simple people need simple things."

That did it! My statement shook John to full attention. Color flamed in his face; his eyes, now angry, focused on me for the first time.

"I'm simple, huh?" he asked. "Let me show you how simply I'll treat your proposal." He grabbed the manila envelope and hurled it in the same trash can that had claimed my business card a week ago.

I slung my handbag strap across my shoulder and set out for the door. Then I thought, tossing my business card was one thing, but trashing my employer's proposal was entirely another bag of beans. John Lim had trusted me to ensure that the proposal got in the hot hands of the exact person so we could compete fairly and squarely with the other suppliers. What good would it do inside a garbage can? That's unacceptable. It was an attitude borne of the hostile environment for so long that it had petrified into a reflex. I turned around abruptly. "Listen, Mr. Begandy, I get paid whether you consider Atlantica's proposal or not. I'm sure you get paid, too, whether you read it or throw it in the trash can before it's read. But I'll tell you what. I'll see to it that your attitude gets some adjustment, if I have to report your rudeness all the way to the Pentagon!" I said, brusquely, and I slammed out of his office, and raced to my own.

Hot all over with frustration and annoyance, I slumped in my swivel chair, considering the move to take next. The most sensible course was to report John to his captain. I mulled this thought over but then decided against it because it had one defect: the need for outside help. I wanted to solve the problem by myself

The sudden ringing of the phone broke my train of thought. It was John. He apologized profusely, swearing he was just kidding me and that he had retrieved the manila envelope from the trash can. He asked if I could go to dinner with him.

From that day forward, John gave me lots of respect and admiration, but in the sales field they did not mean much unless they translated to purchase orders. They never did. I won John's friendship but my competitors got his business. He and the other men simply did not take me seriously as a sales engineer. As a matter of fact, when a competitor supplier threw a lavish party for the sergeants, John always insisted, and succeeded, in including me in the guest list.

After a year-and-a-half with Atlantica, a feeling of job insecurity hit me. Surely, as one of the higher paid engineers in the island, I was getting nowhere fast. Being locked within the confines of sales began to suffocate me. The adventurous engineer inside me wanted to escape. It was time to design a tunnel again that would lead me out in the mainstream of civil engineering.

I set my sights across the ocean. Travel, places, and faces had always fascinated me, and the unknown, intrigued me. I had toured the world through the pages of *National Geographic* in the library. Now I wanted to see and feel the real spots. And the possibility existed because I had a profession, the passport to the good life, according to Father's doctrines on domestic and foreign affairs.

I eyeballed a surveyor's job in Saudi Arabia, the oil-rich country that had been developing its highway systems. Many of my former classmates had gone there to work and they had written me about the sand dunes on the arid desert and about their mysterious women who hid their faces behind black transparent veils. Their letters fascinated me. One friend who came home for a short visit claimed, perhaps to discourage me, that snakes slithered all over the country; that he woke up one morning and found one curled up under his bed. I remained undaunted. I went ahead and applied but the Saudi consul had only one terse statement: "We don't want women over there." He did not even lift his face from his droodling pad to look at my reaction.

I tried Canada, which in the early '60s opened its doors to professionals from all continents. Many of my former officemates in the government, mostly accountants and schoolteachers, had sold their worldly belongings, emigrated there and settled down in places with such exotic names as Saskatchewan, St. Georges de Champlain, and Athabasca. The things they wrote me about, like drive-in movies and snowmobiles and ice fishing and ten-cent lunches and huge salaries made me quiver with envy. I fervently wished to experience them. I applied for admission as an immigrant but the Canadian consulate rejected my application because of my circumstances of being a woman civil engineer.

"Although there are lots of jobs waiting for immigrants, you might not find a suitable one because of your training and experience," the Canadian consul wrote, politely.

The note distressed me. In the past, it was discouraging enough to be rejected because I had no experience. Now, to be told that my background and experience would be a deterrent in finding a suitable job was beyond unbearable. An accountant friend, who had by now established herself in the business world of Vancouver, cheered me up with a sympathetic letter. She suggested that if I learned a traditional skill like typing, she would help me find a job. Inspired by her offer, I attended a class of my women friends who were honing their secretarial skills. Before I could identify the moving parts of a typewriter and swing the basic strokes of Gregg's stenography, however, I discovered I was catastrophically lacking in interest. After the first hour, I reached the conclusion that a traditional skill would not help me over the rough spots of my life.

One day, in my continued search for a land beyond, I discovered yet another way. A friend told me that the United States was recruiting engineers. The news enveloped me with fresh hopes for international travel. While growing up in the slum, I often heard tantalizing stories about America, the land of MacArthur and his men who fought fiercely for the Filipinos during World War II. To my parents and their friends, Americans were true heroes, champions of the masses. America the homeland of these selfless, wonderful demigods was the town abutting paradise. I remember my parents often recount stories of many a Filipino man who had gone to America, became instantly rich, and lived happily ever after. Caught in the whirl of this Utopian imagination about America, my tender mind had been titillated. I had since dreamed of going to America someday.

America! Questions poured out of me immediately. How does one apply? Who are qualified? How long does it take? Next thing I knew I was at the American embassy finding for myself better and more accurate answers to my questions.

# Chapter 8

# Across the Ocean

fter getting registered as a professional civil engineer, I set up an active social life, hoping to recapture the youthful years swallowed by the tough circumstances of engineering school. I had studied hard, worked hard, and by golly, I deserved a good time.

The prevailing morals of the '60s placed the female engineer squarely at the center of gossips, speculations and rumors. Seen in the company of men all the time, most of my neighbors insinuated I was quite the hot number. Others suggested I was gay. Fortunately, I never cared what anybody thought. I wasn't doing anything bad and as far as I was concerned I was through with poverty and pressures, and now, armed with a degree and a good-paying job, life was one great bash for me to enjoy.

I dated interesting men whose careers were as diverse as their nationalities. There was the dark Roman doctor researching malaria for the World Health Organization. An accomplished horseman, he introduced me to a sport of the blue blood, the rich and the famous— horse shows. I watched him dressed in full regalia, guiding a handsome horse gallop, prance, and dance. I never thought horses were capable of such moves. Then there was the talkative, ebullient plumbing and mechanical contractor who was obsessed at earning his first million before age 35. Hooked on the motivational book *Think and Grow Rich*, he might as well have been Napoleon Hill. There was the pale, stoic Czechoslovakian American who had a hush-hush job with the United States Central Intelligence Agency. My parents suspected him of being a rip-off artist. All the men had one thing in common. They could afford the lifestyle to which I was getting accustomed. Father lambasted my unconventional ways. Like other Oriental parents of his time, Father's notions about dating were tightly laced. A man and a woman lustily touching each other's flesh outside marriage were among the contaminated people of the earth, and utterly outside the sphere of respectability, when gauged by his moral standards. And always, always, the woman was blamed for the filth for it was she, the devil, who made the man do it.

"A decent woman does not come home this late!" he thundered at me one night when I came home at ten o'clock. I was twenty-three years old at the time.

"But Father," I said, softly. "This is not any later than when I was attending night school."

Father smacked his right fist across the left, his face twisted in anger. "Don't be reasoning with me. Going to school is one thing, staying out late with a man is another. You are an engineer, a professional. You should be honor-bright." His voice bordered on trembling.

I sat motionless on the stairs, and pretended to concentrate on his lectures. Curious ideas about the Fifth Commandment developed in my mind, but I was not supposed to argue; it was the Filipino way. I simply fumed to myself. *How unfair can you be? All the time I was going to school you never complained about my hours. Was it because I was getting the degree for you? Am I not entitled to a life of my own? Down with this honor-bright business, up with independence!*

"What will the neighbors say about you?" he nagged. "You are not worthy of your degree."

The deliberation with myself continued. *Who gives a damn what those people think? They should mind their own business. I want to be free!*

Then, to keep peace in the family, I offered to move to an apartment of my own. "That way," I articulated, "we'll be living under separate roofs. What I do should not scandalize you"

Father's voice exploded. "No woman ever does that in this country. You stay here until you get married. Then and only then will you be independent of us. When you are married, you will be on your own." His eyes flashed with anger and scorn as he spoke.

I continued to fume inwardly. *On my own after I am married? That's a laugh. It would only mean a change of guard, a different boss. Straight from the father's protection to a husband's home with a new set of rules.* The truth sent a wave of fright in my heart. In a country where a woman's success was measured by the kind of man she snagged for marriage, the Filipino woman was never really free.

The subsequent evenings featured the same nerve-wracking scenario: Father haranguing, Mother by his side, sobbing, and I, a few feet away, seething inside, but resisting the urge to fight back. When Father had exhausted himself, he and Mother would march unceremoniously to their bedroom. I would go upstairs, undress, and fling myself face down on my bed, determined more than ever to leave the country, if only to be free from my parents. The next morning, my hopes fastened around a single word: America, the land of the free. I craved independence.

The door to America burst open in 1965 when the United States' heavy involvement in the Viet Nam war triggered a shortage of technical manpower. To replenish the supply, President Lyndon Johnson approved the recruitment of qualified engineers and technicians from all over the free world.

Ever ready to seize an opening door, I made a thorough evaluation of my qualifications. My continuous employment at H. R. Lopez & Co., Adrian Wilson & Associates, Atlantica Corporation, not to mention the Bureau of Lands and the firsthand knowledge I had gained from our small contracting business, gave me a well-rounded exposure to the engineering profession. Of course, I was qualified to go to America.

I registered my desire to take on President Lyndon Johnson's invitation, and a year of rigmarole and a test of nerves followed. I filled out forms after forms, appeared at various interviews, and presented documents upon documents to prove my qualifications. I practically reconstructed my family tree, which the United States thoroughly and secretly investigated.

My sharpest recollection of that rigmarole was the final interview at the American embassy.

The American embassy in Manila was an imposing white building surrounded by verdant trees, tropical flowers and manicured shrubbery. Part of the first floor was the richly paneled office of the consul assigned to my case. He was a severe man with a narrow face and piercing eyes. While sitting in his swivel chair, he studied the contents of the folder identified by my name.

"So you're a civil engineer. What if you can't find a job in the United States?" he asked, casually.

"Oh, I'm sure I'll find one," I said, my confidence bubbling over.

"That's optimistic," he nodded. "Let's put it this way: suppose nobody wants to hire you as an engineer?"

"I can teach math. I can be a surveyor."

He reached into a desk drawer and removed a file folder. "We want to be sure immigrants do not become public charge—living off of welfare, engaging in prostitution. Remember that third preference immigrants are not required to have relatives or sponsors in the States. Do you have relatives out there?"

## Celia Ruiz-Tomlinson

He was right. I did not have any. Several routine questions followed. Do you plan to overthrow the United States government? Have you ever been insane? Do you have venereal disease? A thorough physical examination was the last hurdle. I submitted myself in fear. Many prospective immigrants had, I heard, been rejected for inconsequential items like having an eleventh finger, hair lice, or for being extremely ugly. The filthy ghetto had toughened my guts, literally. Stomach flu epidemics had come and gone and bypassed me. I had had no illnesses. Indeed, my fears were unfounded. I passed the medical examination. On June 12, 1968, the American consul handed me my visa.

The United States of America granted me a visa! A wave of confidence ran through me. With my visa and my engineering degree as my valiant partners and a new world to conquer, I could hardly wait. I was a born-again person experiencing a real sense of delight about life. I felt a surge of power, as though I could do anything. I was ready to take America by storm and get an exciting job—the engineer to end all engineers!

One night at a party, I met a man who would touch my life. A typical American social gathering over sliced cold cuts and cheese, music, and alcoholic drinks, brought together guests that consisted of American and Filipino residents, and visiting military personnel. I was sitting on a barstool, secretly admiring the skills of the bartender. A bear of a black man whose big hands flew with ease over various bottles of gin, rum, vodka, and other liquids filled orders for mixed drinks. A deep voice from behind broke my concentration.

"Someone told me you're a civil engineer. What's your name, woman engineer?" he asked. To further force an undivided attention, he brushed his leg against mine which were hanging from the stool.

I spun around. We were practically eye to eye with me on the high stool, so I judged him to be close to six feet tall. Deep-set hazel eyes dominated his handsome face and gave away a glint of humor. A mole the size of a pinto bean perched dead smack on the center of his forehead. His vivid mouth emitted an engaging smile. His green fatigues had stripes that indicated his rank of some kind of a sergeant. That explains his lack of couth, I thought. A non-commissioned officer. He's not even a lieutenant, I thought.

Before I could utter my name, he stood up and chased a group of other sergeants who indicated they were going to scout for some "ladies of the evening." My eyes followed him to the doorway. When he turned his head and caught me ogling him, my face burned in embarrassment.

No seductive signals flashed back and forth but in a span of that one fateful moment, a perfect stranger became a potential life mate. I learned afterwards his name was Tom Tomlinson.

Three months later, after I had completely forgotten about him, he reappeared in my office and invited me to lunch. During that hour, our halting conversation drifted awkwardly from the weather to some other trivial matter to another. But there was only so much about rain and chopping coconuts we could cover. I was neither an American nor a person in the United States Air Force to know what a serviceman liked to talk about. He was neither a Filipino nor a civilian who knew how to scratch my interests. For a while it seemed like there was no common ground for us to stand on where we could reach across the cultural barrier.

Then we struck the topic of personal development. As I related to him my family's years of struggle to free ourselves from the depths of seemingly impenetrable poverty, he listened intently, his eyes focused on me in total absorption. He was intelligently quiet. His silence was not the kind that dampened company. Neither was it of the "spaced-out" order. He was intriguingly yet wonderfully quiet. His honest display of genuine interest captivated me.

Thus, my unique relationship with this man who was stationed in Viet Nam began. Once a month, when he flew to Manila to pick up Air Force supplies, we saw each other over dinner, lunch or cocktails, before he went back to Viet Nam. In between those extremely short visits, he wrote long, rambling letters on both sides of legal-sized yellow pads, usually three or four of them. The words he probably could not, or would rather not, express verbally found their way on paper. He wrote and I read. And when we saw each other again in Manila, I talked and he listened.

Language barrier brought the courtship some comedy. In one of Tom's novel-like letters, he wrote: "Last night I played a game of handball and then I took a cold shower." I got stuck right there because I did not know that there was a game called handball. But I had heard of cold showers. How embarrassing, I thought. I looked around me to see if anyone was reading over my shoulder. Seeing no one, I crumpled the letter into a ball and quickly stuffed it inside my bra. Instant size 36! At home I stuffed the letter inside my shoes to make sure nobody in the family read it. I could not take any chances.

How did I find out there really was a game called handball? An American captain came to my boss's office with news. "Joe Blow hurt his eye while playing handball," he reported. This has got to be interesting, I thought, and I dropped the scale and triangles, everything to hear the lurid details. Before the captain's account ended, it became clear to me that there was indeed a sport called handball, much to my relief.

Soon, I thought about the man day and night with an intensity that appalled me. Indeed, after six months of this uncommon relationship, it seemed like I was falling in love. Romance was on the verge of sweeping me off my feet. However, to my careful observation, something seemed wrong. His words, during the few times he spoke, were too responsible for someone who was only two years my senior; his actions too controlled. Following my intuition, I begged his friends to uncover the truth for me. But as though they were bound by the oath of silence, they simply shrugged their shoulders. Left to my own resources, I did a meticulous systematic research through the Air Force chaplain in Viet Nam and alas, I found out he was, like I had suspected, a married man and a father of three children including a set of twins.

The sky caved in on me. It was over. I was a desperate failure as a woman. I attracted nothing but lying married men. But I had been too honest to deserve this. Why me? Why did this man pick on me to amuse himself? My temper flared. I resolved to show him the wrath of a woman scorned.

"You cheat! You liar!" I screamed in great big alphabets across a sheet of paper, stapled it to the letter of the chaplain who had squealed on him, and mailed it to Tom immediately.

Almost before it seemed possible that he could have received my letter, the phone jangled furiously. It was Tom and the chaplain calling, alternately trying to convince me that Tom had been separated from his wife, and that he had not meant to hurt me and the whole soap opera. Tom made a couple more one-day trips to Manila. Each time he saw me, he swore to high heavens he loved me, but never said anything about divorcing his wife to marry me.

"What are your plans then?" I asked, bluntly, while we were having cocktails prior to dinner at a fancy Chinese restaurant.

"I have always wanted to go to Holland," he replied, dreamy-eyed. "I've been trying to pull strings to get stationed in Amsterdam and it looks like I'm getting it."

Tom's reply crushed me because deep within, I wanted to hinge my plans on his, but I decided not to let him know. If he were to break up his family, he would have to do it by his conscious choice and not because of a suggestion from me.

"In that case, I'll tell you my plans," I said with a shrug.

"My friend Lyndon Johnson wants me to come to the United States, so I'm going. I'm a civil engineer, remember?"

"Are you good at it?" he asked, after sipping his gin and tonic.

"Of course, I am" I said, then sipped my own gin and tonic.

"Hey, I'll see you in the States, then," he announced excitedly. "I'll ask for a transfer in California."

He did not know it was too late. I had already decided to go to America alone. "I think you better go on to Holland. That's what you really want. Besides, I have no intentions of marrying below the rank of a lieutenant. You know how it is in the service; the general's wife is also a general. I cannot be a sergeant. Of course, you never said you were going to marry me, either."

"I will not re-enlist," he said as he held my hands. "I've been in the Air Force for eight years. That's enough. I'll enroll in San Francisco State University. I'll see you there. Stay with my sister Trisha in Visalia and wait for me." These, he said in one breath then gulped the rest of his gin and tonic.

I carefully noticed nothing was mentioned about divorce or marriage. "I'll leave on the week of the 12th," I was referring to August, as I considered his suggestion. Part of my mind told me to accept it, but caution about his marital status won out. "We'll see about your sister."

He wrote down Trisha's address on a napkin and gave it to me. We finished our dinner and he headed back to Viet Nam.

To prepare for my trip to the United States, my family fielded serious efforts to raise enough money. Mother smashed the coconut-shell banks she had taken five years to fill. Father skipped pari-mutuel racing for several weeks—a big sacrifice for him. I emptied my bank account. Under the luminous fluorescent light in my parents' room, Mother, Father and I laboriously counted the peso bills and centavo coins on the floor. All together, we pooled the equivalent of approximately three hundred dollars.

It was amazing how the memories of MacArthur had made my parents so agreeable about my going to faraway America to which neither of them had been, when they would not even let me move to an apartment in the same town. The whole family had neither background nor experience to make viable travel plans. We were all clueless how much money would be needed. We were plain ghetto dwellers right to the marrow of our bones.

"Three hundred ought to be enough," I said, my eyes aglow with optimism. "I'll find a job as soon as I get there."

In the morning of my departure, I woke up with a feeling of heavy-hearted pain. To tear out the roots of twenty-six years in order to make a new life as a stranger in a foreign country was not easy. Profound sadness washed over me as I watched my relatives and friends mill about me at the airport, their faces intense and solemn, waiting to say goodbye.

My parents had never trained us, their children, to touch, kiss, or hug as a gesture of emotion, but at that moment, a rush of disconsolation pushed me to embrace Mother. She kept whispering in my ear her "anting-anting," secret words passed down generations and believed to ward off evil spirits. And when I clung to Father's neck, even his sour smell seemed somehow wonderful. But I could not cry. Excitement coupled with some misgivings had frozen my tears.

Father was choked up with emotion. His Adam's apple rolled up and down his throat in a valiant effort to clear the lump blocking his voice. Finally, some words escaped his lips just before I walked toward the airplane: "Show them you are a good engineer."

I looked back as I entered the door marked "For Passengers Only." Mother, in a sudden surge of emotion, bawled and squalled, as the send-off party turned around to drive home.

Then at last, it was over. The hugs and good-byes were only fresh memories now. I sat in the coach section of Pan American Airlines, armed with three hundred dollars, a suitcase, the consul's envelope, my college records and diploma. I was ready once again to set the other side of the globe on fire!

The plane taxied the runway of the Los Angeles airport, culminating a fifteen-hour flight, my first long trip. When I stepped inside the Immigration and Naturalization hall, I had an awful sensation of having walked into a nightmare. The sea of people's faces of various shapes and colors reduced me to an insignificant dot. They moved about coming and going in different directions. I did not realize so many people, not just myself, wanted to come to America.

It was not until I had set to leave the hall that the enormity of what I had done dawned on me. I had no particular place to go. Then, it hit me. I was alone! Independence. I certainly had got it now, but with only three hundred dollars, my papers, and a visa for a new life in America. The first wave of real panic rippled through my body. Nausea rose inexorably within me. Endure, body, endure, I whispered inwardly. Sudden fear of the unknown, jet lag, exhaustion—as I sorted out its causes, it became clear I wouldn't be able to halt it. My pulse raced and the sweats began. I turned and dragged my suitcase to the restroom. There, I had my first rude awakening. I could not open the toilet door unless I inserted a dime in the slot. Momentarily, the calculator inside my head buzzed frantically, solving a basic arithmetic problem: at the rate of ten cents per relief, how long will three hundred dollars last? My knees weakened. I did what was inevitable and sauntered back to the lobby, where I sank myself, now weak, into one of the vinyl chairs. The palms of my hands cupping my face, I took a deep sigh in frantic despair. I could not go at it alone. I desperately needed someone to direct me for the first few hours, at least.

San Francisco, where most Filipino immigrants went, came to my mind. I hopped on the first plane to San Francisco, my heart beating frantically. Upon arrival at the city atop rolling hills, I ransacked my carry-on bag for my little directory. It was a small black book that fit in the palm of my hand. On the first page, it said—1968 Diary. It had blanks for statistics, which I had filled out dutifully. Name Celia Suva Ruiz, height 5'4," weight 135 lbs., birthdate 1/25/42. Pages of listings of monthly birthstones and wedding anniversary terms followed. Then came the pages filled with American phone numbers of friends and relatives of friends' back home. While letting my fingers do the walking on the pages of the black book, my eyes were suddenly riveted at the name Carlos Tejuco, personal friend of John Lim.

I had thought John Lim had no interest in my well-being, and neither knew nor cared how I felt, but when time came for us to part, he had given me Carlos Tejuco's address and phone number, along with a thoughtful advice. He had said, "When looking for a job in the States, don't show the Americans you are overly eager. Make them feel and know that they will hire you because you have something to offer in return. Play it cool."

The address and phone number of Tom's sister Trisha leaped from the list. I remembered Tom's last word in Manila: "I will not re-enlist. I will see you in the States. Stay with Trisha. I'll see you there." Could I count on him?

I decided to call Carlos Tejuco, counting heavily on Filipino hospitality.

Within minutes, Carlos and I were in his station wagon on the way to Pacifica. I stared unseeing as the evening darkness drew out the glitter of San Francisco. Carlos, a slight man of Chinese heritage, talked about the beauty of San Francisco like a tour guide, but failed to impress me. I had already begun to feel the dawning of reality; the pressure of having to find a job for survival in this new world.

"Don't worry about it," Carlos said thoughtfully to calm my fears. "Last week, three young Filipino engineers from my wife's hometown stayed with us. They just picked up the phone, and pronto, they had jobs. Engineers are in demand these days."

Carlos's wife, Mila, gracious and pretty with her black hair greeted me with a warm smile when she ushered us into the house. She had prepared a Filipino meal of steamed rice and spicy pork and chicken, which she insisted I should eat.

After the meal, she ushered me to my room for the evening. Closing the door behind me, I proceeded to the window where I could see the lights of the sprawling metropolis. My heart sank. The idea of tackling this strange world alone chilled my hands. I tried to warm them by jamming them into my armpits.

"This city is going to devour me," I whispered, fearfully.

Shuddering, I pulled the drapes, undressed, turned off the lights, and curled up in a fetal position, covering my face with the smooth sheet. Fortunately, fatigue weighed down on me down and I slept peacefully, momentarily oblivious of any further misgivings.

# Chapter 9

*The Descent to Hell*

**1968,** the most tumultuous year of the decade. In a span of two months, assassin's bullets snuffed out the lives of Senator Robert Kennedy and Reverend Martin Luther King, Jr. Students seized control of buildings at Columbia University in New York, and the Democratic National Convention in Chicago became a battle zone as anti-war demonstrators clashed with police and Illinois National Guardsmen. An exciting time for introduction to America.

It was almost noon when I awakened to see a foggy sky and potted green plants hanging by the window. I stretched my neck to look out. So there was America: concrete walks, splendid houses, cars cruising up and down black asphalt streets. I didn't know what I had expected to see in a Utopian place, but what was out there gravely bared a hard fact: America is just another place on earth where people worked to live. Nowhere was the exciting wonderland my parents dreamed I'd stumble upon. I searched for a crowd out there welcoming me with hats and horns. Not a peep.

When I had showered and dressed, I went to the dining room where Mila was bustling. Her husband and two teenaged children had already gone to where their day propelled them, and she was now cleaning up the room, which was still heavy with the aroma of garlic-fried food.

Mila and I ate a light meal, and then we flopped in the car for a ride around San Francisco.

"You better see the city before you start looking for a job," she said, laughing. There was a genuine mirth in her laughter.

She drove up and down steep streets, through quaint-smelling

73

markets, and along a wharf thronged with curious crowds. I stared unseeing. The urgent need to find a job lurked in my mind. I needed a place of my own. Two days—it was all I'd spend with the Tejucos. Not more than two days because we were really strangers.

The nagging problems flooded my mind all the way home. As soon as we were in the house, with Mila's permission, I started to sift through the yellow pages.

"Unplug the phone and take it to the den so you can have privacy," Mila thoughtfully suggested.

I placed the telephone directory on the coffee table in the den after clearing it of women's magazines. Comfortably positioned in a soft couch, I started with the construction companies.

"My name is Celia Ruiz, I am a civil engineer and I am looking for a job," I recited with a slight uneasiness.

"We don't have an opening right now," a young woman with a sugary voice answered. "I'm sorry."

"May I file an application with you?" I persisted.

"We normally hire men only. You might want to try other companies."

I called three others in quick succession. All had a common response: they wanted men only. As I stared at the fourth listing, a paralyzing fear gripped me, sending my stomach to a series of knots. I'd never find a job then? This was terrifyingly reminiscent of the days after graduation, when I was applying for a civil engineering position at a furious rate and being turned down at a more furious rate. I closed my eyes as if to pray. Then, it dawned on me to try the engineering firms.

With unsteady hands, I did just that. Again the responses were typical: male engineers only. After the fifth call, I numbly stopped. It would be best to apply in person. The employers must see my résumé if they were to be convinced of my training and experience.

I managed to get past the receptionist of one company, but as soon as I introduced myself to the personnel manager, I received shocking news.

"We hire only men," said this avuncular man. "I don't think you'll ever find a job as a civil engineer anywhere." He politely shoved the unopened envelope to me; his stare fixed on my eyes. Stunned, I stepped back, and out, and rushed to my host's house. In my room, I burst into tears, my face buried in a pillow. But the man's soulful eyes kept looking up at me, reminding me, sadly, of my doomed future. Sobs of helplessness racked my whole body. All my strength seemed to have deserted me.

When self-pity flickered out, I weakly rose and walked to the window, where I stood, looking out. There was America again. But it was blurred. Slowly, the vision cleared up, and freshly developed black and white pictures of the past weeks in the Philippines unfolded in my mind. Clips of my family frantically raising the pocket money for my trip to America, where grandeur and vast riches awaited me. Clips of my brothers and sisters frantically serving food to friends and relatives who had come for the send-off party. Clips of Father who might still be in Bulacan, bragging about his daughter, *the engineer in America* showing Americans how it's done. Take that, right in the gut, he was probably saying.

The idea of returning home a dismal failure staggered me. I could not imagine facing my parents, brothers, sisters, friends, and acquaintances as a desperate failure. Mother would rant for the rest of her life about the money wasted on the airfare and pocket money. She would equate six hundred dollars with countless cavans of rice that could have fed the whole family for years; to thousands of yards of material she could have sewn into clothes that would have kept every sister and brother covered rain or shine. I could just hear her voice. In her basic accounting, she would talk of how she could have invested the money in tons of fish and how it would have multiplied in profits. Though unmentioned, for her, my trip was a sure-fire investment. And even as a small-time investor, she had not been known to fail.

I could clearly envision Father, who had always regarded me as the reincarnation of himself as a professional, depressed for the rest of his mortal life because of my failure. He would never again set foot in his hometown because he would be afflicted with interminable shame. How could he face his folks who had rooted for me, *for him*, for each little success *we* had attained? He would see me as a pathetic figure fallen from the pedestal. He would greet me with jeers and derisions. My failure would be a stiff rod that would flog him to his slow death.

Beads of perspiration formed above my lips and under my eyes. There were no other options available; I must stay, painful and uncertain though it might be.

Daunted, but definitely hopeful, I could reverse the tide once more like in the past. I picked up the phone receiver and dialed a dredging company. The result was negative. I tried a couple of construction suppliers next. And two more. All responses boiled down to "no." Even M. D. Burns & Co., Atlantica's correspondent in San Francisco, refused to hire me. It looked ominously as though I must move on. For the next few minutes, my mind churned until one thought stood out: the possibility Tom was serious about seeing me in the States. My heart lurched. It was my last and only chance now that my hopes of establishing life on my own seemed shattered. Buoyed by this new hope, my fingers flew over the telephone as I dialed Trisha's number. I pressed the receiver against my ear, and waited anxiously, as though my survival in the States hinged on this one phone call. The telephone on the other end rang incessantly for a good minute before someone picked it up. It was Trisha!

The conversation between Trisha and me picked up on an upbeat note, as if we were long-lost friends. Her easy friendship erased my fear of rejection. Soon, she was giving me directions for the bus trip to Fresno.

On the way to Fresno, the broad-shouldered Greyhound bus driver and I cheerfully conversed on various trivial matters, he looking up at the rearview mirror where I could see his gentle green eyes wink at me. When the subject of my profession came about, he suddenly shut up.

The crowds flowed like tide at the Fresno bus station. Watching people operate the vending machines helped ease my anxiety in waiting. Curious about the automatic soft drink dispenser, I ambled towards it, inserted a dime, and pressed a button. Instead of shooting out a bottle of 7-UP which I had selected, the machine told me to "make another selection."

"I'll buy you one someplace," a man breathed at my neck from behind, jolting me.

He was about my age, dark and muscled, and wearing greasy gray coveralls, his big hairy hand wrapped around a bottle of Coke. On the pocket of his coveralls was machine-embroidered the word "Greyhound."

"No ... no, thanks," I said, waving my hands frantically. I only wanted to see how the vending machine works. I've never seen one before."

He ignored my refusal and followed me to the bench where I sat.

"Come on," he urged. "I'd like to know you." He advanced and flung his arm across the back of my seat, around my shoulders. I moved to the edge of the bench.

"You're new in the country, I can tell," he remarked.

"How?" I asked, incredulously.

"From your movements. You're gonna work here?"

"Yes."

"What kind of job?"

"I'm a civil engineer."

He looked at me with an enigmatic expression, picked up his Coke, and scampered down the opposite end of the hall.

Trisha and her family arrived at the bus station, quickly diverting my attention to my new situation.

Immediately, I took on the details of my new hosts. Earl, boyish with his crew-cut chestnut hair and slight build, carried an 18-month-old girl in one arm, and held a four-year-old boy in the other, leaving

Trisha free to greet me with a light hug. She was pretty, big-boned and stood very straight, and there was an extreme cleanliness and delicacy about her person and the way she kept the babies immaculately dressed and groomed.

The family whisked me to a station wagon and we were on our way. Awkward silence dominated the one-hour drive to Visalia. The quiet broke only when I admired the baby's soft, curly blond hair and the little boy's shiny pomaded hair or when Trisha pointed to an item of interest along the highway.

Trisha led me to my room in their house that had wide windows and high ceilings supported by exposed wooden beams. For the first time, I gawked in wonder at the amazing array of mechanical appliances I had never seen before. My mind had been too distracted with problems that I did not notice them at the Tejuco home. The washing machine that agitated and washed dirty clothes; the dryer that whirred and clattered as it tumbled and dried clothes; the dishwasher that did everything for Trisha after she had scraped the leftover food from the plates.

On my second night at Trisha's, I picked up the local newspaper, thinking the job situation might be different in Visalia. The dismally thin newspaper consisted of two or three news items and a sprinkling of boat-related ads since Visalia's prime industry was boat-building and selling.

Trisha and I soon loosened up, drawing out each other's trust and enthusiasm. Through her stories, I pieced together a family that grew out of logging camps from the northwest. I found out more about Tom than what I had personally gathered from our dozen one-day dates.

It was strange that although from the very beginning, my life had grated against the world because it didn't fit its contours, somehow some events seemed to have happened as if they were meant to smooth things out for me. Tom, indeed, left the Air Force, and on my fourth day in Visalia, he phoned Trisha and instructed her to put me on the first plane for Albuquerque, New Mexico.

At once, I was euphoric on the plane. I might make it yet in America. Being a true chronic optimist, I reflected on what would happen, or what I wanted to happen. Tom would enroll in a university. With his financial help, I would be able to concentrate on finding an engineering job if it took a whole year; we would fall madly, madly in love, marry, and be absurdly happy.

The shrill whine of the motors of the airplane as it readied to land on the Albuquerque airport broke my thoughts. I peeked through the window and saw vast arid desert soils of reds and browns and a sprinkling of structures. On my way into the waiting room, I quickly spotted Tom among the many faces. Something inside me pushed me to throw my arms around him. I felt the warmth of his body, looked into his eyes, and wondered if my own reflected the same blaze of love. It surely felt good that everything was going to be all right.

Tom introduced me to those who had waited with him. Peggy, his mother, fiftyish, fully erect, was nearly six feet tall and seemed to look down on the world. She definitely looked down on me at my height. Clay, his father, same age, balding, robust. He also had what seemed like the family trademark: a big mole on the forehead.

Once more, I was whisked from an airport, but this time, to a motel called The Sundowner where we went to the coffee shop. Booming greetings and hearty good exchange of stories gave me a clearer picture as to why we were in Albuquerque, New Mexico, a place I did not know existed in America. Peggy and Clay had driven to Albuquerque from their home in Arizona to pick up vehicle parts. As Roads Superintendent for the Bureau of Indian Affairs, Clay maintained and operated the Navajo tribe's pool of heavy equipment. Peggy worked as a bookkeeper in a high school in the Indian reservation. They had asked Tom to meet them in Albuquerque upon his discharge from the service. They had not seen each other in four years.

When the conversation began to wind down, Peggy suddenly stood up. "I don't know what everybody's problem is," she declared, "but I'm going to bed. I paid for three rooms, if anyone cares to know."

She dipped a hand into her purse and dug out three individual keys; each attached to a plastic key holder bearing the hotel's name.

"Three?" Tom asked, surprised. "Why three?"

Peggy responded quickly. "One for your Dad and me, one for you, and one for her. She's a single girl, isn't she?" She was almost disdainful.

Tom gazed at me tenderly. "I think we really just need one room, Mom."

An uncomfortable silence fell. It was not in fact going to be a unique experience to be with Tom in a room. Our one-day trysts in a plush hotel in Manila and in a lush mountain resort up north came to mind without effort. Recalling them, the familiar sensations returned. It seemed thrilling and romantic in the beginning, this togetherness in the confines of four walls, then when it was actually happening, there was always a feeling of unease, as if my parents' eyes were peering through some unseen hole on the doorknob. There was never really total privacy. The feeling stiffened me. The events struck like a tornado. Next thing I knew Tom and I were heading for one room, his arm around my shoulders, mine around his back.

Tom unlocked the door and pushed it gently. He flicked a switch on the wall and instantly, the cold dark room brightened. When the deadbolt on the door clicked, I knew we were now isolated from the rest of the world.

A painting of Indian pottery on the wall summoned my attention but my eyes wandered back to the room's most prominent furnishing, a meticulously made bed. I shuddered but before my mind could function, Tom pulled me, and without resistance, I went into his arms.

I woke up the following morning with three things in my head: a splitting pain, confusion, and red eyes. I was still reeling from the swirling tide that had carried my life into uncharted waters. It was incredible. Suddenly, I was a "married" woman. I remembered the child I had been in Bulacan, naive and innocent. Could I be the same person? Weighed down by guilt, I despised the turn of events, but I felt helpless to change it just there and then. I numbly rode the tide. It was all I could do.

A bright morning dawned. Tom and I had breakfast with his parents at the same hotel restaurant. Beyond the clatter of spoons and forks and the humming of conversations of other diners, I was conscious of Peggy's penetrating stares. In my guilt-riddled mind, the pupils of her blue eyes were the point of a drill etching the word "whore" on my forehead for the love I had made with his married son. All the unpleasantness I had felt the night before came rushing back. I simply couldn't throw off the suffocating Oriental moral I was brought up with no matter how I tried. It was imbedded deeply in my brain.

Then I came face-to-face with a few economic realities. Except for a few dollars in his pocket, Tom was stone-broke. He had quite nothing except for an estranged wife and three little children to support. He had one thing going for him: he was deeply rooted in America. He knew where the wind blew and would know how to sway with it rhythmically.

We moved to a cheap one-bedroom apartment later on, using part of my pocket money for advance rent. Located on the top floor of a three-story building, we climbed several flights of stairs. Using some more of my pocket money, Tom bought of all things, a mop, a broom, dishwashing soap, a dust pan, dish towels, cleansers, and other housekeeping items. The last item at the bottom of the supermarket sack intrigued me: a hardcover book with the red-and-white checkered design of tablecloth on its cover. A *Better Homes and Gardens* cookbook! His shopping spree left me a little more than fifty dollars. Peggy and Clay, whose hearts were genuinely filled with generosity, gave us old pots and pans and filled the refrigerator with meats and vegetables to last us a month.

Tom took a part-time job as a partsman at a heavy equipment supply store, and enrolled at the University of New Mexico. With his estranged family in Texas to support, his G. I. Bill assistance and $40 weekly salary barely provided for the two of us. Nevertheless, I was somehow content, though terribly guilt-ridden.

I settled into a daily routine so novel that I found it momentarily fascinating. I fried eggs and toasted slices of bread in the morning and had breakfast with Tom. He usually left for his job by seven and returned about noon. Alone in the apartment, I spent time in the public laundry, reading instructions on how to operate washing machines, dryers, and vending machines that dispensed small boxes of detergents, fabric softeners, and bleaches. Then I browsed through the pages of my official cookbook to start working on our lunch, and to plan ahead for supper. Mopping the floor and scrubbing the toilet bowl got in there somewhere between noon and six o'clock. As each day passed, I realized how little housework I had done in the Philippines in spite of poverty. My parents had tolerated my using schoolwork as excuse to avoid dishwashing or cooking.

When things around the apartment were settled slightly, I wrote my family that Tom and I were married in a small civil ceremony, a lie necessary to stop Mother from nagging me across the ocean and to halt Father from condemning me to a defiled life. The family seemed pleased with my report, and every member asked me to send American material things. Mother wanted dollars, younger sister wanted cosmetics, older sister wanted shoes and pantyhoses, younger brother wanted a basketball, and older brother wanted a tape recorder. Every time I opened a letter from home, a list of "purchase orders" popped out.

One afternoon, while I was picking over pinto beans on the Formica kitchen counter, a series of loud knocks startled me. I jumped to my feet to respond. I latched on the security chain before I opened the door just a crack to see whom it was knocking with such urgency. It was Mike, Tom's younger brother.

"Open it," he grunted impatiently.

Reluctantly I did. As the door yawned, Mike, suitcase in hand, walked briskly past me. He was as tall and lanky as I remembered him from our brief and only encounter in Manila when he and Tom had spent their rest and recuperation week. He headed to the refrigerator and helped himself to a glass of milk.

"Where's Tommy?" he asked as he returned the half-gallon carton of milk in the refrigerator. He turned around in anticipation of my answer. His eyes had the hint of more blue than green, his hair a lighter brown than Tom's. Only crooked teeth and dark gums marred his handsome face when he spoke. He wore a gray sweatshirt the sleeves of which had been cut off.

"At UNM," I said watching him now take off his socks then his shoes.

"I'm tired," he complained. "I've been on the road since last night." He plopped his body onto the living room couch and fell asleep almost instantly.

Memories of Mike's conversation in Manila came flooding back. He had laughed at unusual things, like the success story of a Negro doctor; or at the idea that younger brother Joe would marry a Navajo girl. Odd things had infuriated him, like the Air Force dentist's question if there was Negro blood in the family because of pigmentation in his gums.

Tom and Mike had shared a lot before my time. They had been stationed in the same camp in Viet Nam. They had shared the same bunk bed. War stories had it that they had been shot at together, but survived, during the Tet offensive. Now it seemed like they might be together again in this apartment. An ice cube slid into my heart.

Mike had already unpacked and was sifting on the couch, smoking a cigarette when Tom appeared at the door.

"Hey, look who's here!" Tom exclaimed, extending his right hand as he walked towards Mike. Mike ground the cigarette butt on the ashtray then grasped Tom's hand tightly.

Happy greetings and reverberating Viet Nam stories ensued. From behind the kitchen counter I could tell the brothers were overjoyed with their reunion after a couple of months of separation. Mike talked about his plans of going to computer school on his G. I. Bill, perhaps supplement it by working part time at a Circle K store. Throughout my listening to the men's chatter, I never heard anything about Mike looking for a place of his own to stay.

I split a fried polish sausage three ways and served each piece over hot boiled pinto beans. During dinner, I ate quietly while the two men continued reviewing the immediate past.

The following morning, after Tom and Mike left for their day's program, I looked in dismay at the mess around me. Dirty dishes on the counter, a pan on the stove, cold burnt scrambled eggs stuck to it, overflowing garbage can in the kitchen, unmade bed in the bedroom, a full hamper of dirty clothes in the living room. Mike's tenancy was official.

The latest addition to the family changed the complexion of my routine. Now I woke up each morning to cook Tom's breakfast, but first I cleared the counter of Mike's soiled cereal bowls. After breakfast and the men had left, I hauled their dirty clothes to the laundry. I discovered rudely that I hadn't perfected the art of laundering because one day, Mike was visibly upset when he felt his shorts still damp from insufficient drying. He angrily tossed his clothes back to the hamper and gave me a look that slapped my face. He was at the apartment at 4:00 o'clock but waited until Tom came home so I would serve the food on the table. During dinner he dominated the conversation with racist topics. After eating, he walked away without neither a grunt of thank you nor an offer of help in the clean-up process. His intrusion into my life began to tear me apart.

As that grim summer passed on, I managed to keep functioning, but barely, towards the end of my first month in the apartment. Most of the time I was in a kind of stupor. The drudgery of housekeeping, Mike's lowly treatment of me, waiting for Tom's divorce to happen, and lying to my parents about my wonderful life in MacArthur's country took their toll. Then one day, my frustrations somehow all broke loose. I wept and screamed: "I did not come to America to slave for two grown white men! I did not come to America to disgrace myself, to stoop so low!"

Finally, torn between the guilt of cohabiting with a married man and the indignity of being treated like trash by his brother, I mustered the necessary strength to bolt out of the arrangement. Tom and I parted amicably, promising to see each other frequently.

Henceforth, on the beginning of my second month in the United States, I set out on my own again, morally battered but not beaten, in both worse and better shape. Worse, because I had only fifty dollars in my pocket. Better, because, I had grown wiser to the ways of America.

# Chapter 10

# An American Man's World

lmost overnight the hot summer vanished. Refrigerated air wafted from out of the blue, touching and changing lives along its path. The leaves on trees, once green and supple, turned rusty and brittle. Humans, once free and lightly clothed, wrapped themselves and walked around with hands jammed into their pockets. There I was, wrapped up in mismatched sweater, jacket, coat, earmuffs, bonnet, cap and hood—all donated by Peggy and her kind friends. It was late August. I found that something strange happens to the brain when it is cooped unnecessarily. Every time I was bonneted, capped and hooded, I kept thinking it was not a question whether I would win a Nobel Prize for engineering in America but how many.

It was the beginning of winter when I left Tom to move to the Young Women's Christian Association. Dragging my suitcase filled with my worldly belongings, I walked in the door of the YWCA, and saw a lobby with a sprinkling of women waiting for health classes. Some lounged around in black leotards while others sat patiently on couches, stroking babies' foreheads. On one wall was a bookcase filled with an assortment of books on fitness and general well-being. A large coffee table dominated the lobby, covered in disarray with women's magazines. Through another door, I could see a bare spacious hall and some more women milling about.

I had known that aside from giving low-priced classes, YWCA's around the world also rented rooms to decent young women as part of their youth development program. I had talked to the housemother, Mrs. Blanche Hutton, over the phone earlier about the possibility of me becoming a boarder. To qualify, she had said, I must be no younger than fourteen and no older than twenty-three, of good moral character, and able to pay eight dollars weekly rent. By osmosis, I became just that. I projected myself as a naive sixteen-year-old who would soon be employed sacking French fries at a Lotaburger store. Fortunately, perhaps as my prize for resourcefulness, Mrs. Hutton did not cross-examine me. She had simply asked me to come over; there was room. She would expect me this morning. I glanced at my watch. It was nine o'clock in the morning, the appointed hour.

"Is Mrs. Hutton here?" I asked a pretty black woman wearing a turban of colorful psychedelic designs and hoop earrings.

Mrs. Hutton herself welcomed me. Gray-haired and motherly, big but not fat, Mrs. Hutton ran the YWCA's boarding program. A pair of reading glasses was perched on the middle of her nose. Her waistless printed polyester dress hung loosely over her enormous hips. "You are very lucky, honey, one of my girls turned twenty-three last week and I told her to move out," she said with an air of unquestionable authority as she stuck a folder into a brown metal filing cabinet. "She wanted to stay, but I said na-ah, rules are rules. I keep them until they're twenty-three and that's it. Gotta make room for the younger ones." She collected the notebooks in front of her and stacked them neatly to the side. "Did you say you're fifteen?"

"No ma'am, sixteen." My heart contracted with the lie. I glanced around the room to avoid her eyes that might penetrate the falsehood in mine. I knew, however, I could easily pass for a fifteen-year-old, especially in my faded jeans and Tom's old white shirt, and my long straight hair which I had worn tumbling over my shoulders. In the apartment complex that I had just left, mothers used to flag me, asking if I was a student at Valley High, and if I would like to sit for their babies. Some of our neighbors had curiously inquired if Tom was my father, thinking I was an adopted Korean orphan. Nagged by the constant screening at places where alcohol was served, Tom had taken me to the courthouse to get me a twenty-first-birthday identification card. My looks covered up my real age.

Mrs. Hutton reached for a sheet of mimeographed paper from the filing cabinet. "Here is a list of the rules and regulations. Read it. I'd say the most important thing is for you girls to get along well," she said.

She aroused my curiosity. I asked, "How many girls are living here?"

"Twenty–four, two girls in each room," she answered.

I skimmed over the three pages of rules and regulations. It included upkeep of rooms, kitchen privileges and responsibilities, telephone usage, curfew hours, and rental payment, and many other restrictions.

When Mrs. Hutton saw me tear my face from the rules and

regulations, she continued. "I don't tolerate long phone calls and breaking of curfew hours. Everybody must be in the premises at nine o'clock at night, no later, no exceptions."

She squeezed her huge body out of the cramped office space, into a narrow hall, and continued talking, explaining the rules in details, as she led me upstairs. "You girls are responsible for the upkeep of your rooms. The mops and brooms are in the janitor's closet, as well as the floor wax and dust cloths. The rules are rather strict, but otherwise, this is really a nice place to live."

A ghetto might have been more apt. A series of bedrooms separated by a dark corridor lined a wing of the upper level of the decrepit building. The dank, ventless community bathrooms and toilets—there were two of them—at the end of the hall reeked of urine. Grime ringed the bathtubs, which had yellowed from old age and abuse. Slime and black mildew blotched the shower curtains.

I marched alongside Mrs. Hutton to another corridor leading to the kitchen and dining room and a sitting room crowded with old dusty couches of unmatched designs. Several teenaged black girls sat in front of a television set, munching corn chips, reading magazines, and giggling.

"You girls supply your own food. We have provided the kitchen conveniences. They are in good working condition." Mrs. Hutton pointed at the appliances.

A gigantic refrigerator reared its presence at the end of the dining room. Two gas stoves flanked the refrigerator. Pots and pans of aluminum, scratched Teflon's, chipped porcelain, heavy cast iron, and plastic margarine tubs filled a large single-compartment sink.

"You girls take turns cleaning the kitchen. Every week I put out a Nightly Schedule of Kitchen Keepers. It must be followed strictly. If a girl does not do her job the night she is supposed to, she will be scheduled three nights in a row the following week. If she refuses to do it, I throw her out in the street. I cannot be bothered with girls who do not want to learn good behavior." There was cold iron in her voice.

I looked at the growing pile of eating utensils on the sink. It was already a foot above the surface and half the day had not passed yet.

Mrs. Hutton led me to one of the bedrooms. She inspected her list, looked up at the number at the top of the door, and when she was sure it was the right one, pounded it with her fat clenched fist.

"Open the door, Dolores!" she demanded.

The door squeaked open, and it revealed a real sixteen-year-old Hispanic girl. Instantly, her love for the color pink became obvious. The large pink curlers that pulled her black hair from her face doubled the size of her head. Her short pink nightgown bared brown skinny thighs. Pink furry slippers swallowed each of her entire foot.

"Show the room to Celia, your new roommate," Mrs. Hutton ordered and she huffed back downstairs to her little cubbyhole.

Dolores took over the grand tour, as directed. She said, "This is it!" gesturing to the eight-foot-square room furnished with two single beds. A narrow strip of space barely enough for one person to walk through, sideways, separated them. "I will mop the floor Monday through Wednesday. You do it Thursday through Saturday. Mrs. Hutton inspects the rooms everyday except Sunday."

I agreed with the proposed division of labor.

A small window with dilapidated blinds provided some natural light to the room. She demonstrated how to open and shut both. She pointed to an open closet the size of a telephone booth packed with colorful dresses of different lengths. She closed it, then showed me a small empty drawer. "I have been here longer than you have, so the privilege of using the bigger closet is mine. You know, seniority system. I had to wait till my former roommate moved out before I could get it," she explained almost apologetically. "When I move out, you can have it."

"It's okay," I consoled her. "I don't have much to put in a closet, anyway. I'll just leave my clothes in my suitcase. If you want to use the drawer, too, you may also have it."

She thanked me and added, "I probably won't be here much longer. My boyfriend and I will be getting married soon. I'm pretty excited." She showed me a finger wearing a gold band with a microscopic piece of diamond.

I held her hand close up to scrutinize it. "Alright! Do you have a wedding date in mind yet?"

"No, but I can hardly wait."

All in good time, Dolores gave me a glimpse of her life. She had dropped out of high school and now worked as part-time cashier at a Woolworth's store. She was not yet eighteen years-old, therefore, her parents were still obligated to help her pay her rent at the YWCA and some other bills. Staying at the YWCA was an acceptable alternative for them in lieu of formal schooling. She had no desire to go back to school. What for, she said, when she could get a GED which is just as good as a high school diploma. All she wanted was to fill her hope chest and get married and let her future husband, a sheet metal worker, support her.

Dolores's bliss of contentment was defeating. Not knowing was a blessing. Undereducated and ignorant of more ambitious propositions, little pleasures provided sufficient pomp in the pageantry of her meager existence, while mine demanded more than what two states of the United States of America could supply.

The deplorable condition of my new home rolled back memories of the Manila filth and cockroach-infested public market squalor, but thoughts of the uncertain future won over mulling about past discomforts. The cramped room served my basic shelter needs. I was going to miss Tom at every turn, which I could not do without bumping into Dolores. Even if Dolores and I warmed up to each other in friendship, my nights would still be cold, for she could not replace Tom. For a moment, but just for a moment, I wondered if I had made the right decision to move out of the apartment; that perhaps instead I should have implored Tom to ask Mike to move out. But the thought of Tom's marital status quickly reassured me that I should have no regrets about my decision.

A considerable chunk of my life had gone into adaptation to various facets of poverty. There were times, in moments of self-evaluation, when I wondered if they had been too much. On more occasions than I cared to remember I had to come out of difficult situations, much like having to squeeze my whole being through tiny saw-toothed holes. Each time I had made it, I was surprised at how much capability a human being possessed to shrink and adjust to the shape of the opening in order to make it through. The life I now faced at the YWCA was just one such hole. My being had already begun to flex to the new shape of things.

The following morning, I woke up early to see what everybody was up to. I filled a cup with hot water and sipped on it in one corner of the kitchen while watching the girls in various stages of preparation for the day ahead. Some black girls sat all over the dining room, spooning milk-soaked cereals to their mouths. I heard one girl belting out a song, her off-key voice competing with the splash of the shower. The other young women, dressed and made-up, paraded down the stairs to leave the building. By nine o'clock everybody had left. When the dust settled, the sink overflowed with dirty bowls, glasses, plates with leftover food, pancake turners stuck to greasy pans, a chopping block, crumpled paper cups, spoons and forks and garbage. One unfortunate girl would tackle them tonight, in strict compliance with Mrs. Hutton's Nightly Schedule of Kitchen Keepers. It would take her at least two hours to clean up the mess that twenty-four girls created in a few minutes. I shuddered at the grim thought of the inevitable advent of my turn. I shoved the depressing thought to the back of my mind and went out for a newspaper.

Job ads filled the classified section of *The Albuquerque Journal*. To my delight, they were classified according to discipline instead of by sex. I read the section from one end of the page to the other. My eyes wandered back to an ad specially printed in darker ink: CIVIL ENGINEER 14K APPLY SNELLING & SNELLING EMPLOYMENT AGENCY. I nipped the ad out of the newspaper with my fingernails and hummed softly to myself, then smiled. Why not? Agents, I had always known, earn commissions. They know their market and they work hard. They have got to try harder to find me a job to make money for themselves. Yes indeed! And I continued humming, and spent the rest of the day finding out about bus routes and city streets.

A sunny Monday morning greeted me when I strode out the YWCA. Armed with the envelope filled with my papers and the newspaper clipping, I boarded the bus that would take me to Snelling & Snelling.

I had barely stuck my head at the agency office when a tall older woman whose well-coiffed platinum blond hair was lacquered securely in place, and with enormous red jewelry dangling from her ears, stood up and greeted me at the door.

"Come on in, honey," she said, and led me to a narrow but well-lit corridor.

Impressed by the aggressiveness of the agency's employee, I followed her as ordered without any idea what she had in mind, until we reached the end of the hall, where she pushed a door. It opened to a room full of typewriters.

"What are you going to do to me?" I asked, although I had an idea.

Her painted eyebrows went up. "Why, I'm giving you a typing test, what else?" she asked, scathingly.

I looked up to her, aware of the beginning of a grin on my face. I thought, then giggled.

"You see, ma'am, I'm a civil engineer, and I came here about this ad." I dug the clipping from the envelope and handed it to her.

She read the ad, looked down at me then at the typewriters, and broke into hysterical laughter, which was so contagious that I laughed right along with her. "I'll be damned," she said when she found the breath to talk. "I've never seen such a thing in my 25 years in the employment agency business." She wiped a tear of laughter from her eyes. "I'll tell you what, honey, it's going to be difficult but we'll give it one hell of a try." With that, she started working on my case. She set up an interview with Gordon Herkenhoff & Associates, a reputable engineering company not too far from the YWCA. She told Mr. Herkenhoff the young lady engineer would be there in an hour.

Dead center of a well-appointed office, behind an L-shaped desk sat Gordon Herkenhoff, president of the company. In his late sixties, with a big nose and a pockmarked face, he exuded a distinguished air in his gray business suit. On the wall behind him hung various college diplomas and awards of appreciation for his valuable contributions to society.

"Come in, honey, I'll interview you," he greeted me with a smile that bared acres of teeth.

Standing motionless at the door, I wondered at the moment why there was no chair in front of Mr. Herkenhoff's desk.

"Where do I sit?" I asked, hesitantly.

"Around the table, honey he answered, motioning

I walked behind the desk, as he had indicated, and I saw the seat intended for me—three inches away from his lap!

I put on my inscrutable face and planted myself solidly into the armchair and pretended as if what we were about to do was normal to all interviews. I glanced casually around the room, then stared down at his knees when they started to rub against mine. "Excuse me," I said, as I discreetly rolled my chair just a shade farther back.

He launched into a dissertation about his tour of duty in the Philippines during World War II and the current race to space between Russia and the United States. Then, he asked me a few inconsequential questions, like when I arrived and where I was staying. One small topic led to another and when I found an occasion to inject into the conversation something about the estimates that I had prepared including that for the Manila Hilton, he talked about Conrad Hilton. He had been his buddy, he said, and rambled on about their youthful days. Then he came to the bottom line of the interview. He was going to hire a man.

Undaunted by my report, my employment agent set up more interviews with engineering and construction company presidents. Some did not want to be bothered; they told her they were not interested in a female engineer. Others asked her to send me over, out of curiosity. Finally, sheer exhaustion overcame my fearless agent. Her green eyes were dull, unlike at the start of her mission to find her "little one" an engineering job.

"Honey, why the hell can't you just be an ordinary little girl? Better yet be a go-go dancer. A new lounge has a job order for a pretty Oriental waitress. Topless." she said.

I looked at her. "That's it?" I asked. "You can't find me a job?"

"That's it." It was the first time she had ever quit on a client.

I walked towards the door in slow, reluctant steps. There was this gnawing feeling of disappointment. If an employment agency could not be of help, who could be? Before I closed the door behind me, I turned my head to bid farewell to my agent.

I continued to scout for a prospective employer on my own, being more familiar with the kinds of work a civil engineer could do. I tried suppliers of construction materials. The responses were typical: they employed salesmen. I tried banks, but personnel managers said they did not need engineers as appraisers. Would I be interested in training as a bank teller? I went to Albuquerque Public Schools to see if they needed mathematics teachers. This approach ignited a small spark of interest. I was cordially welcomed through the ranks but my early hopes were soon dashed when I met the top man.

"We do need math teachers," the superintendent, a kind, small bespectacled gentleman assured me. "But I'm afraid your accent is much too thick for the kids. They might not understand you. They'll find that as a good excuse when they flunk the subject."

Hearing that, I drew a mental line over one of other possible jobs I had thought I could be doing in lieu of civil engineering.

I came home broken after each day of pounding the pavement in search for a job. Then, eternity came with my turn to keep the kitchen. It seemed like I had a dirtier kitchen to clean and more dishes and utensils to wash than the others. When the bottom of the sink finally appeared, I stretched my neck from left to right, from front to back to exercise the whiplash away. Fortunately, the flip side of my double life offered some entertaining features. The real YWCA teenagers, happy as blue jays in their naivete, unknowingly perked me up. When we gathered informally in the dining room at night to talk about how each girl's day went, they asked silly questions that helped banish the depressing thoughts out of my mind temporarily. How do people in the islands get around? Are the boys groovy? Say something Philippine. When I did, they broke out in laughter. The sound of chuckles provided me with a refreshing break from all my troubles. But when I climbed on my bed, they came rushing back.

Convinced I would have to enter the civil engineering arena through some other indirect doors, I headed for the land surveyors. The initial responses were negative. Then, Tom's father told a friend of his, a practicing surveyor, about me. I phoned him. He sounded enthusiastic about hiring me, and gave me directions to his place of work.

On the way to his office, I could not believe the sudden stroke of luck. A surveyor was hiring me sight unseen! Could a door be opening now? I would soon find out.

"Red Morrison Surveying Company" the sign read on the door of an office flanked by a day nursery and an Indian jewelry store. Inside, the place showed evidence of the surveying business. There were reels of tapes, bundles of wooden hubs, red plastic ribbons, and markers. I saw no employees around other than Red Morrison so I surmised they were out in the field.

A big barrel-chested man, Red Morrison's bald head glistened like a billiard ball. His face was scalded-lobster red. He had a ready, somewhat fixed smile on his face, which towered over me a good deal. After asking me a few questions, he told me I could start today. He led me to a computer, and showed me its keys and its wonders.

The machine was an awesome sign of progress. I ran the tips of my fingers around it, admiring its engineered construction. I poked at a key just to see what would happen. Surveying technology had certainly come far in America. Gone were the days of the logarithm books and hand-cranked calculators and the old standard blank forms.

"I used to do everything manually. Now this machine will do everything for you," I gushed in disbelief.

"Try solving this problem," Red said, handing me a sheet of paper containing survey data. He pulled a chair close to mine. He watched quietly as the machine completely absorbed my attention. I entered a number here, pressed a key there. I watched it spit out numbers. Then I felt something awful happening. A cautious light movement above my knee grabbed my attention. I looked at my lap. Red's hand was crawling up my thigh under my skirt! I looked at his face. It had a peculiar sort of concentration. I felt a stab of fear. My heart beat so loud I could hear it. Blood rose to my head and my face and neck became sticky hot. The force of fright ejected me from the chair like a projectile.

LADY IN A MANHOLE. In 1977, *The Albuquerque Tribune* featured on its front page Celia, "the first woman civil engineer to do field inspection full–time for the city."

In 1966 Celia received her certificate of registration as Civil Engineer Number 7704 from the Philippine board of examiners.

# ALUMNI SECTION

Mary Jane D. Pabalan, Alumni Section Editor

# Celia Ruiz Tomlimson

When Celia Ruiz (MIT BSCE 1964) left the country in 1968 to search for greener pastures abroad, she knew the path she was taking was rather risky. Yet, despite the odds, she believed that one's drive to success would not be so difficult if one had the necessary guts, patience and persistence to reach what is to be achieved.

After 17 years of work as a civil engineer, and being blessed with a husband and a child, CELIA RUIZ-TOMLINSON deserves respect and recognition — she has been making waves and hitting it big in New Mexico, USA. Celia has had the distinction of achieving the following "firsts": First and only foreign national admitted by the New Mexico Board of Registration for Professional Engineers based on reciprocity; First woman field engineer/inspector in New Mexico; First woman to qualify for the New Mexico Land Surveyor's exam.

At present, Celia works as Design Engineer for the City of Albuquerque aside from being engineer/consultant to land developers within New Mexico.

Despite being stuck in a job which has long been signified to be a man's profession, Celia has definitely no regrets. With it, she believes, there has never been a profession where she could find much challenge and pride — that is why she hasn't settled for anything less.

One should be surprised, looking into the determination and dedication of this young lady who has had so much belief in her profession. Bringing along her diploma and barely enough pocket money, Celia grabbed the opportunity to work in the United States, arriving in Los Angeles with no particular destination and hardly an acquaintance.

When she saw her pocket money was dwindling, Celia was desperate. Nevertheless, she turned down offers of other jobs not within the

**TOMLINSON**

field of engineering.

Finally she landed a job as a Junior Designer at the Albuquerque City Hall. This, however, did not end her troubles yet — it was just the start of a hard battle between her and her associates. Being oriental-looking and petite, she was sarcastically discriminated at the work place — she was refused by subordinates, harassed by older draftsmen and was always left out during engineers' parties and meetings. Equipped with a lot of self-confidence and a glib tongue, she gradually beat all the odds, accomplishing what has to be done. She believes that in every task she undertakes, success is sure to follow. And success she had.

Today, Celia is accepted with great respect by her peers. She has come a long way despite being the underdog in a man's world. The secret, she believes, is the ability for self-expression. "In this country, I am by myself," she says. "I would truly be paralyzed if I didn't know how to speak for myself. I never expect anybody to go out of his way to speak for me."

Being a woman-achiever, Celia was listed in Who's Who of American Women starting from the 11th edition, 1970. She has also graced the front pages of the Albuquerque Tribune and the Employees' Newsletter in Albuquerque, New Mexico. Born January 25, 1942 to

Mr. and Mrs. Felix Ruiz, Celia hails from San Miguel, Bulacan. She is the second in a brood of five. Belonging to a family of humble beginnings, Celia had to contend herself with the hard times during her infancy because of the war. Mr. Ruiz had one obsession, though — he believed that giving his children the best education was the sure way to success.

During her youth, Celia had the inclination towards writing, dreaming of becoming a journalist someday. On one occasion, being only an alternate, she easily won an on-the-spot feature-writing contest as representative of the M.A. Roxas High School.

Celia, however, was fond of meeting new dimensions and had the tendency to look for more challenges. She found out that she could very well apply her talents in Civil Engineering. She finished the course in 1964 here at MIT (no less) and easily passed the board exams the next year.

Before leaving for abroad, Celia had worked for various firms in engineering and construction such as being surveyor for the Bureau of Lands, 1960-'65; engineer, H.R. Lopez and Co., 1965; estimator, Adrian Wilson and Associates, 1965-'66; engineer, Atlantica Corporation, 1966-'68.

Celia is happily married to Thomas E. Tomlinson, a utilities contractor. At present living in a subdivision in Albuquerque, New Mexico, the Tomlinsons are blessed with a five-year-old boy named Thomas Clay.

Celia, with success in her hands, never fails to look back. She has combined the guts of a man and the charm of a woman to achieve her goals. She deserves to be honored, to be emulated — because here is one lady who has accomplished much our Institute could very well be proud of. And our country as well.

Celia celebrated her debut in 1960. It was held on the street in front of the public market. A dog and barefoot slum boys attended the party.

he debutante flanked by proud parents Felix and Anacleta. Behind them is the four-meter square stall.

Celia's father fenced off a portion of the street temporarily to afford Celia and her well-wishers some privacy.

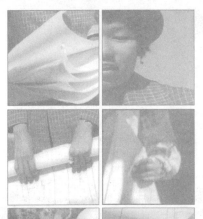

The tireless and hands-on founder of Rhombus Professional Associates in her office . . .

. . . and at the job site.

# The Lady Engineers Spicy Meat Dish

by Gina L. Young

When Celia Ruiz Tomlinson, Albuquerque's pioneer woman engineer, is not designing septic systems or street grades for a housing subdivision, she can be found up to her elbows in soy sauce in her kitchen. Briskly wielding a cleaver and expertly transferring various aromatic ingredients from a stone grinder to a red wok, she concocts such exotic dishes as *gising-gising* and *tokwa't baboy*.

But her favorite, which she likes to share with friends, has a less intimidating twang to it. Called Venison Orientale, the dish is as simple as it sounds.

"Venison Orientale is a dish for those special happy times when good friends get together and I want to honor them with a great meal," Celia says as she mashes fresh garlic in the stone grinder. "Venison is my choice for this recipe, but beef is just as tasty. This main dish brings out the meat's fine, fresh, natural flavor with just a light coating of delicate spicy sauce."

The Philippine-born self-styled chef confesses her fondness for staying around the kitchen. "I'm like a homing pigeon to it. Can you think of a more natural place to go in a house?"

She also delights in comparing cooking with engineering. "They are similar. The same terms are used. You talk about *draining* vegetables, *measuring* flour, *sawing* lamb bones. Engineering and cooking are arts of constructing something. Something good, hopefully." Then, she recalls her deep personal satisfaction when she succeeded in her homemade yeast bread the first time. "I felt the same kind of enjoyment when I finished my first tongue-and-groove wood joint in my carpentry class years ago."

Celia, who became Albuquerque's first woman field engineer and inspector in 1977, loves the challenges of cooking. "When I was new in the United States, I knew zero about it. I tried following cookbook in the beginning, then la improvising a little bit here and the Soon, I found myself enjoying my periments. Now, using different her and spices, it's like chemistry class over again!"

The following recipe is, according her, part Filipino, part Korean, p Hawaiian, easy to make, tried a tested, and the most requested by friends.

### Venison Orientale

1 lb. tender cut venison
(beef or lamb may be used)
¼ c soy sauce
¼ c pineapple juice
2 cloves garlic, peeled and mashed
1 T sesame oil
½ c onion, finely chopped
1 t MSG
Salt to taste
Freshly ground pepper to taste
2 T butter

Cut up the meat into thin slices. Ma nate it in the mixture of the next eig ingredients for at least 1 hour. Just befo eating, stir-fry the meat in butter in a p over high heat until most of the liquid gone. A little amount of medium th sauce should remain, coating the me slices. Serve over hot steamed ri Serves three hearty appetites.

Celia (with son Thomas) was presented the 2004 Filipinas Magazine Entrepreneurship Achievement Award in San Francisco, California.

## *The Metamorphosis*

### By Ernie Delfin

## Celia Ruiz Tomlinson: A role model among Filipinos in America in search for their place in the Sun

Reading and playing chess are two of my favorite leisure activities which I can do both at Barnes and Nobles Bookstores near my home in Orange County. Although I read very few books by Filipino authors, it was a sheer delight to have discovered an autobiographical book written by a lady civil engineer from Bulacan, Philippines who is now a successful entrepreneur businessperson in New Mexico.

I have never met the author, Celia Ruiz Tomlinson yet through e-mails, phone calls as well as a through a new E-forum called, ProgressiveTimes, that I created, it seems that we have known each other for more than a decade. Through another friend, Linda Nietes from Palos Verdes who owns a Filipiniana Expressions Bookshop, I

*(Continued on page 6)*

*Celia Ruiz Tomlinson*

In 1983, Celia founded Rhombus Professional Associates, Inc. in Albuquerque, New Mexico. Initially a civil engineering and surveying company, it has evolved into a full-service engineering and environmental consulting firm composed of engineers, surveyors, scientists, and technicians.

THE FAMILY (seated from left to right): Son Thomas; daughter-in-law Ana; stepdaughter Mic stepson Michael; the author Celia; and husband Tom.

# Chapter 11

# The New Beginning

I was sitting on my bed, head bent over the classified section of the afternoon paper, when the door opened. I raised my head and saw Gracie. She motioned me to head for the kitchen.

Gracie, a Puerto Rican, was nearly five feet tall, chubby, and with a great deal of kinky brown hair that kept falling forward over her wide, square shoulders. She walked around constantly eating doughnuts and fancy sweet rolls, a habit sustained by the proximity of a bakery to the printing shop where she worked. She became a friend because there were two things to which both of us could relate. One, she had been raised in California among Filipinos and two, she acted more mature than the other teenagers did. In addition, she found in me a receptive listener to her stories of excitement about her current engagement to a rookie policeman, after I parried all questions about myself, to avoid complications concerning the secret of my other life.

I joined Gracie in a davenport. She dug her hand into a brown paper sack and pulled out two of the simpler baked goods I had seen with her: cupcakes with chocolate icing. She gave me one and kept the other to herself.

"Listen," she whispered, while peeling the corrugated paper off the cupcake. "There will be an opening for a counter girl in the print shop. I thought I'd tip you ahead of the other girls." She sank her teeth into the cupcake and continued talking through a full mouth. "It's really easy work. You just make copies of stuff and collect from the customers. You don't even have to use your head. Maybe a little, for some addition and multiplication."

Five years of age separated us, but watching and hearing Gracie, I felt the gap wider than it was, perhaps twice as much. It came, I surmised, from my having gone through more trials and tribulations out there in the world. Life certainly had a lopsided, unfair way of tossing out troubles. Some people caught novelettes, others sagas. It was the second time I had been conscious of the difference between the YWCA girls and me. The first was when an epileptic Mexican offered to recommend me to her boss at a tortilla factory to sell packaged corn tortillas to the lunch crowd at the adjoining Mexican food restaurant. I wondered how long I should keep the girls, Gracie in particular, in the dark about myself. Lately, coming up with excuses for not accepting their help seemed to be getting more difficult. But then again, if I told them the truth about my degree, they would not understand, and they would come up with more questions I would really care to answer. It was simpler to keep the situation the way it was. The less they knew the better for me. It was a proposition that was not hurting anybody. The girls' offer of odd jobs helped renew my faith in the innate goodness in people. The newspapers also featured daily ads for waitresses and domestic help but I resisted them no matter how scary my financial situation was becoming. But of course at the YWCA, everybody economized in her own quaint way. I was down to zero breakfast and an apple for lunch. Once in a while, I financed a cheeseburger, but most of the time, it was a can of cheap Norwegian sardines eaten hurriedly with a glass of water in the stillness of my room. Tom, in spite of his being broke, took me out occasionally, and we splurged on pizza. Otherwise, for a normal fare, the cupcake like the one in my hand was "high standard of living."

One time I saw a tall lean black girl with a bush of an Afro hairdo screaming profanities, her head bobbing. Another, a big black one, wagged a finger at her and yelled more expletives. The other girls, Hispanic, a Cherokee, and Anglos took sides and tried to pull their fighter away, like a tug of war. The more each troop tried, the more aggressive the provoked leader became. Within a minute, Mrs. Hutton's heavy footsteps pounded the stairs as she raced upstairs. When she arrived, the agitated girls were on the verge of a head-on collision. Like Goliath, Mrs. Hutton sandwiched her monstrous body between the two mountains of teenaged strength and in one big shove broke up the warring forces. "Stop this fighting now or I'll throw you girls out in the street!" Mrs. Hutton thundered. Her huge arms now bent like a bow on her hips, she was an imposing figure no one dared to challenge, and she knew it, and used it to the hilt in running the YWCA's boarding program.

The girls, who lived in holy terror of her, disbanded and went their separate ways. No one wanted to be around in case Mrs. Hutton opted to give her the third degree. No one wanted to lose the precious privilege to live at the YWCA for eight dollars weekly rent. If they did lose their berth, they'd be forced to return to the houses of their parents most of whom were still supporting them financially. And they'd have to abide by their parents' rules again. That would cramp their styles. At the YWCA, all they had to do was keep their rooms clean and observe the curfew hours. In between, they led an unsupervised lifestyle. They did not have to explain their activities to Mrs. Hutton, although lately, there were rumors that Mrs. Hutton had briefed the other ladies of the board of directors about the need to poke their noses into the girls' activities. She had received a few menacing calls from strange men who wanted her to furnish them with women for the evening. She had smashed the telephone receiver against its cradle in response. But until such time that the policy-makers put a new rule in writing and enforce it, no one had to know what the girls were actually up to. Where else could anyone find such a haven?

I reflected all these in amusement, and switched my thoughts on my own teenaged days. They had not been anything like this. They had been drab and uneventful in terms of physical challenges. No fist fights, no athletics, no sports, and no odd, menial jobs. How great it felt now to be among the teenagers. Here was the perfect opportunity to live like one and experience what I had missed. After all, how many people get a second chance at youth?

Finally, the door to a decent employment yawned for me. A small partnership called Associated Land Surveyors hired me. One partner, Frank Benavidez, a fortyish Hispanic, had a face designed to smile, all its lines curving upward. Short and heavyset, but light on his feet, he chattered continually, fluently in English and Spanish, on upbeat subjects and one-line sex jokes. He punctuated them all with a bombastic, contagious laugh.

Frank's amiable air quickly put me at ease on my first day. He said that while at the bank he had overheard two engineering consultants talking about a "cute young Filipino woman engineer, a fresh immigrant" in hot pursuit of a job. He offered, and I accepted, employment at $2.50 an hour, while I kept making applications with engineering companies.

"I understand your position," he smiled, directing the lines around his eyes and lips upward.

Frank definitely understood. He was known for giving part-time jobs to foreign students of the University of New Mexico. Understandably profit-oriented, he and his partner, paid rock bottom salaries knowing the students were in a bind. Law of supply and demand. Students needed him more than he needed them. He contended he was giving the students valuable experience, and therefore, he was entitled to get the best use of them before they became smart and moved on to more generous employers. It was a cycle in life, he believed, every young person must live through.

Frank did not have to expound on his business beliefs; they were fair enough for me. I needed the exposure, more than a decent salary, to get my feet back on the track of engineering.

Surveying is an integral part of civil engineering. Just about every civil engineering project begins and ends with a survey. Before a structure is designed, the land on which it will be built is surveyed for boundary and to document if it is flat or sloping or a combination of both. Before concrete is poured for a wall or a sidewalk, a surveyor marks its exact location on the ground. After construction of a permanent structure, a surveyor measures and certifies its location.

Working with surveyors definitely gave me an edge over working with busboys, printers, and tortilla makers. It brought me to within walking distance in case the door of opportunity to an engineering job suddenly swung open. With my newfound job, I wore many hats. I answered the phone and took messages for Frank and his partner who were always out marketing or doing survey work. I drew outlines of houses on lots. I typed, using two fingers on a clunky manual typewriter, legal descriptions of properties for banks and title companies. I filed the correspondence in the metal cabinet and the plans on the racks. I did light housekeeping, putting plans and equipment where they belonged. Somewhere in between, I found time to know more about the only other employee, Oliver Trujillo.

Oliver performed the same duties I did. In addition, he operated the blueprint machine, delivered drawings to clients, and picked up copies of records in City Hall, the County Courthouse and engineering companies. He had a face only his mother would love. A wide space separated his front teeth and his eyes were slightly out of focus. He laughed heartily and generously, especially about his stories of his many girlfriends who were, according to him, only after his body. A hardworking young man with a morbid sense of humor, he called me "Fea," Spanish word for ugly. I returned the compliment by naming him "Guapo," Spanish for handsome. We became friends quickly.

A good friend indeed, he had become. One day, coming from back City Hall with rolls of prints tucked under one arm, he barged into the door with a huge grin spread across his face, exposing his spacy teeth. His other hand held a paper sack that indicated he had bought his lunch at Steak in the Rough.

"Fea," he cried, as he dumped rolled plans on a drafting table. You're gonna love this news, Fea." He delighted in stressing the name he had assigned me. He used it either in the beginning or ending of each statement. "Fea, the City needs a junior designer. I saw it on the bulletin board. It has been tacked there for a long time, the guys told me, I just never paid attention to it until now that I know you're looking for an engineering job."

The thought of a door of opportunity fixing to open planted a grin on my face.

Oliver beamed, judging from the glow in my eyes that he already made my day so early. We climbed on his blue battered pick-up and off we flew on the freeway to City Hall.

A seven-story concrete building houses the city offices at the heart of downtown Albuquerque. The fourth floor held the drafting room, a reception room, private offices of chiefs, and a spacious conference room where "the powers that be" scheduled an interview for me.

Anxiety over the forthcoming interview sent me tossing and turning in bed, thinking of all the possible questions and the best answers to them. Immigration particulars, education, work experience, their details—I sorted them out in my mind. When I could no longer contain them lying down, I leaped to my feet and ransacked my suitcase for my papers. I sat on the edge of my bed and read every word on my immigration documents, résumé and letters of commendation. Soon, my eyelids were heavy with sleep. I lay down and placed the papers on top of my stomach. Sleep sneaked in without my knowledge.

The following day, dressed in a simple cotton blouse and skirt, I set out to face the challenge of the interview.

The climate of the unique interview was set around a conference table in the office of Erwin Hensch, Director of Public Works. Bright sunlight penetrated the east picture window, casting a glare on the giant Albuquerque street map, which was pinned to the south wall with thumbtacks. The white-plaster wall near Hensch's desk displayed his two engineering diplomas and registration certificates from two states. Framed pictures of bridges and drainage canals adorned the wall opposite the picture window.

I slipped into a chair about halfway down the long rectangular table. At the head table was Erwin Hensch, whose mission was to oversee the city's street maintenance program, engineering, liquid waste or sewage operations, solid waste or garbage collections, and water resources management, and to take responsibility to the public in matters of public works. The eight other men around the table were either his division heads or administrative assistants.

The arrangement reminded me of the Last Supper but instead of bread and wine, some of the men in business suits had doughnuts on square wax paper and steaming coffee in Styrofoam cups. Erwin Hensch called the meeting to order. Everyone stiffened to attention. He scanned his troop with an air of authority. Pleased that all his subordinates' eyes were dutifully focused on him, Hensch announced item number one on the agenda of this particular staff meeting: interview of Miss Celia Ruiz, applicant for Junior Designer!

## Celia Ruiz-Tomlinson

From the dark suit that he wore, to the blond straight hair parted neatly on one side, to the way he cocked his head when he spoke, Hensch was a man who delighted in being the center of attention. He enjoyed giving a performance. A vein that prominently crossed his forehead from an eyebrow to the hairline seemed to be the speedometer of his words and thoughts. It bulged when he spoke louder.

I glanced at the men around me, and when I looked down, I was proud to see my steady hands, in case the engineers were watching. Feeling in complete command of the situation, I pulled myself erect. My hair was in a bun to give me a more matured look, baring an anxious face ready for questions for these men whose eyes were studying me, like generals watching a pass-in review.

"Miss Ruiz, you are the first woman engineer ever to apply for this job. Why did you study civil engineering?" asked Hensch, abruptly.

"Why not?" I asked, acting surprised.

A subdued laughter hummed about the small audience.

"He meant what made you go into civil engineering? You know, it's not everyday that we see women applying for a civil engineering position. Girls don't normally study to become engineers," a Hispanic man with black handlebar moustache on a square face qualified Hensch's question.

I had answered that question several hundred times more than I cared to remember but I ran through briefly, but conscientiously, how Father, an all-around construction man, had convinced me into getting a diploma for him. The answer might just mean very much to them.

"You did it for your father?" asked a bony man incredulously, following several puffs of his pipe, which he kept within three inches of his mouth all the time.

"For myself, too," I answered. "Somewhere along the way it became my own choice, and a challenge. I kept telling myself I'd stick to it as long as I could tackle it."

Copies of my résumé were passed. Like a group of diners studying the menu in a restaurant, everyone studied his copy in silence. When they were done, I waited anxiously for questions about my experience as an engineer. But no one asked. Instead, Hensch talked about the only woman classmate he had in engineering school whom nobody heard from after graduation. Women did have the tendency, the other men added in various ways after telling of their own female classmates, to fade away after school was done.

"Which reminds me," Hensch interjected, "Do you have a boyfriend and does he intend to stay in Albuquerque?"

"I do have a boyfriend but he has no plans of moving," I said, aware that an answer to the contrary would wipe out my chances for the job.

The forum switched to lively stories about the Philippines during the war and to small talk about places to see in New Mexico, and recommendations for Chinese restaurants. Then, at last, when everyone ran out of juicy accounts of travel and adventure, Hensch wound up item number one on the agenda and politely dismissed me.

"We'll notify you, one way or the other," he said, suavely and charmingly. Then he added, "Don't call us. We'll call you." And he laughed.

The interview, meaningless and empty though it was, left me with positive vibrations. Hensch's curiosity if I had a boyfriend who might affect my permanence in the city hinted a favorable forecast. I could hear another door in my life slowly squeaking open!

# Chapter 12

❦

# The Bottom of the Ladder, Part I

ireworks lit the sky; confetti flew when I received the news that City Hall hired me as Junior Designer. Within my mind, the festivities reached towering heights, mending my confidence that had been bruised by the earlier series of drawbacks. I treaded on air between Dolores' bed and mine at the YWCA cubbyhole, whistling zesty tunes.

That night, Tom came for me and after swearing by Mrs. Hutton's stern reminder of the curfew hour, we celebrated my success in landing an engineering job. We feasted on a large combination of pizza with extra cheese, and since it was a big occasion, we poised ourselves for a big pitcher of ice-cold beer. In between bites of the stringy pizza and slugs of brew, I babbled in exhilaration about the "doors" in my life, how they opened sooner or later. Tom smiled and smiled and quietly exuded genuine happiness for me. Throughout our dinner, cozy warmth filled my heart. I had a job now and I was gushing about it to the only person close to me in this strange country.

When I walked inside the door of the YWCA building after dinner, I glanced at the big clock on the wall of Mrs. Hutton's office. It was still a few minutes before nine o'clock, but Mrs. Hutton had already planted herself behind the counter like a sentinel. Seeing me walk in, she turned around to check the clock behind her. She nodded at me in approval of my good behavior. I stepped forward to the front of Mrs. Hutton's counter and looked, smiling at her face. I was fighting the overwhelming temptation to share with her the good news about my new job and how much money I'd be making each month. It was probably more than what she had ever made as den mother.

"Can I help you, Hon?" she finally asked after noticing the silly, entranced look on my face.

"No, thank you." I decided against letting her in on my secret. It was not yet time. I was no different from the teenaged girls. I also lived in holy terror of her. I was also clinging tenaciously to my eight-dollars-per-week space. Instead, I left her the sound of my footsteps as I raced up the stairs, leaping over two steps at a time. After peeling the clothes from my skin, I plopped my naked body in bed and pulled the sheets over my head. I closed my eyes, and in my mental vision, a glorious sun arose to usher the dawn of the end of my struggle. But sleep wouldn't come. I kept wondering what type of people I'd be working with and what kind of work I'd be doing. After all, this was a different country. A brand new world.

Engineering has its unique, beautiful features compared to other professions. Basic engineering principles are universal, unlike those of law or medicine, which vary from country to country. Engineering has no cultural taboos. Also, engineering is a pleasant means of livelihood. It's a job not carved out of human misery. While the lawyer is hired by a rape victim, and a sick person needs the physician, the engineer is commissioned to work on constructive things meant to improve the quality of life. He builds roads and bridges for safe and efficient movement of people and goods; he builds dams to generate electricity; he designs systems to process human waste. Granted, a disaster occurs occasionally, like the bursting of a dam or the collapse of a bridge, but those are rare exceptions.

Instead of counting sheep, I extolled the many wonderful virtues of the civil engineering profession, and I finally fell into a deep, dreamless sleep.

I woke up before the sun was up the following morning. I wanted to be early for work. It was important to make a good first impression. After dressing up and inspecting myself critically in front of the cloudy mirror in the bathroom, I went to the kitchen. I raised a cup of hot tea to quietly toast the beginning of my life as an engineer in America. The light had at last beamed on my dark corner. My private war had ended. It was time to rest my battle-tired mind and concentrate on being a civil engineer.

It was not to be. I was barely crossing a new, hostile frontier.

When I stepped out of the elevator on the fourth floor of City Hall, the lost look on my face prompted an older engineer to greet me. He had a wrinkled face. His receding auburn hair made his drawn face appear longer. His loose lips parted easily, showing stained, even teeth. A victim of a debilitating muscular disease, he leaned against the wall to keep his balance, losing a couple of inches from his tallness.

He extended his shaking hands to me and his crumpled face distorted in what was meant to be a smile.

"You must be the new girl," he said in a raspy voice.

I reached for his hand and introduced myself. "Pleased to meet you. I heard a lot about you from the guys who interviewed you. I'm Bob Blair." His speech was blurred. "Are you looking for the boss's office?"

When I said yes, he motioned for me to follow him.

I stayed close to him as he walked with very short steps and slowly along the wall. We passed two engineers' private offices, one of which was his, through a drafting room, and then into another private room. The occupant looked up and moved his green eyes from Bob to me, as if wanting answers to his mental questions.

"This is Frank Bailey, our boss," Bob said. "And this is Celia Ruiz, the new Junior Designer." After a small exchange of greetings, he hobbled out of the room and left me with Frank. I took in the details of the man in front of me.

Everything about him seemed short. He was short and stocky. His short hair was prematurely gray for a man of thirty-five. He chewed nervously on a short pencil when he was not talking, making his thin lips virtually invisible. When he smiled, short crowded teeth showed. Several short pencils ravaged with teeth marks laid on top of his desk. He spoke in short sentences. He talked about his job; he had just recently been promoted to head the Drafting and Design Section. I figured it was not a major position, otherwise he would have been one of the apostles at the interview. He also talked about my job and the Pakistani man who last held it and quit less than two years ago. Over the same period that the position had been vacant and publicly advertised, no one had applied. Hensch, he said, was forced to hire me because there had been no other applicants and the pressure had been on to hire one. A woman engineer was better than no engineer, was the impression I received.

"Well," he said, quickly rising to his feet, "let me introduce you to the draftsmen." He led me to the drafting room. As I followed him, I confirmed his height. His head was just slightly above my eye level.

The drafting room filled with a rustling of whispers when we entered. As Frank took me around, the drafters, consisting of older Caucasians and middle-aged Hispanics, huddled in small groups and cast occasional glances at me. The men spoke in hushed voices, but loud enough for me to hear their conversation.

"Here's the new engineer," a rotund, pudgy, Hispanic character with a moustache said in an audible whisper. "Let's see how long she'll last."

"This isn't fair to Fred," said another dark man. He did not raise his face from the drawing board on which he was engrossed printing letters. "He's been doing design work for years. Frank should have promoted him instead of hiring a woman engineer." He stopped talking when Frank and I passed by his desk. But I could feel the weight of his eyes on my back.

The moment finally came for me to meet the Fred of every draftsman's concern. Fred Gomez, was in his early thirties, bespectacled, and with a deep commanding voice. He had attended two semesters of civil engineering and with that, he qualified as engineering technician, a responsible position slightly above all draftsmen. He had access to the engineers who, in turn, delegated their authority to him. He was to become the common technician for design engineer Bob Blair and myself.

Frank led me towards three draftswomen. However, they sensed us coming and walked out of the room to avoid us. Frank continued straight ahead and introduced me to a shrunken, pale, old man who was wearing a hearing aid in each ear. The man leaned forward, extended his hand to me, and whispered, "Do you think you will acquire some class if you worked here?" and he grinned.

I showed him the ghost of an enigmatic smile. "Something," I whispered back at him, leaving him totally mystified.

After the round of introductions, Frank pushed a scarred table against Fred's. "This is your desk," he said. He reached for a chair and rolled it behind the table. With that, he left me in the drafting room.

I looked in dismay at the arrangement. A dark green telephone, an in-out tray, a specification book, a pile of rolled plans, and a telephone directory partitioned my work area from Fred's. To the right of the demarcation line lay his territory; to the left was my bailiwick: a table and a chair. The chair's last occupant must have been a heavy person who tilted himself forward in a launch position a lot. Before trying the oddly shaped seat, I glanced enviously at the private offices of all the other engineers.

A sharp silence and an avoidance of eyes reigned between Fred and me during the first few days. Although he appeared to be a reasonable individual, I could feel his resentment; something was griping him. I reflected it was his loss of direct access to Frank. Worse yet, he must go through me. As a technician, he sat on top of the ultimate goal of a draftsman, but for lack of the prescribed education, he could never become an engineer. Although his work was essential, a technician only existed in the shadow of the glamour of the engineer. He interpreted, using crisp curves and straight lines on reproducible paper, the idea of the engineer. There were times when he injected his own viable concepts but these, having originated from a lower caste in the engineering society, were usually suspect. If the idea worked, the engineer received the recognition. Money might have been a sore point, too. His salary was a lot less than mine was. If someone considered his five-year head start, and ignored my five years of schoolwork, it did seem unfair.

One day, when the telephone on our demarcation line rang, his resentment surfaced.

"Answer the phone," he grunted, in his deep voice, his eyes focused on a sheet of tracing paper on the drafting table.

My hackles stood on their ends. Did my ears betray me? I studied Fred's face. His lips were tight, his face frowning. He was dead serious. This man actually ordered me to pick up the telephone, the same telephone he had been answering without question every time.

"Why?" I was direct.

"This phone is for the whole drafting room," he mumbled. He was now drawing little circles using a protractor.

"So?" I shrugged, attempting to get him to look at me.

"So answer it!" he scowled, then looked squarely at me, his cat-eyes magnified by the thick lenses of his glasses. "You're closer to it than anyone else."

I pulled myself erect, twiddled my thumbs, and set my stare at the opposite direction. This was a critical moment. My life as an engineer in the United States of America depended on the way this situation was handled. Questions chased one another in my mind. What if the phone rang many times during the day? He had answered it every time. If I followed his order, what would he tell me to do next? Did he expect me to yell out the name of the person called or did he want me to approach him or her? This seemingly trivial matter, if not handled wisely, could form a dark cloud that would hover over my career. This first impression could make or break me as a supervisor. In the end, I decided to resist.

"I'm not answering the phone for anybody." There was iron and finality in my voice. "You take it, and if it's for me, let me know." I nonchalantly turned my eyes on the plans I was working on.

The phone jangled sharply. Fred ignored it. All right, I thought, if that's the way you want to be. I ignored it, too. Finally, after the nth impatient ring, he gave in, to my surprise. He grabbed the phone so brutally I feared for a second that he would smash it over my head. A moment later, he was saying "Fred speaking." He listened, expressionless, then said, "I'll see what I can do, ma'am. I'll call you back." I breathed out with a whoosh of relief. I had surmised correctly that he was a reasonable person.

From that moment on, Fred treated me with a little more respect. He accepted my implied message that in the totem pole of engineering, the engineer was a notch above the technician. He answered the phone dutifully when it rang and when he left the room, he assigned a drafter to answer it. But he launched one more effort to push me to the ropes.

Work flowed from engineers to drafters then back to engineers. The engineers sketched, the drafters drew in final form, using their natural talents or aided by drafting machines. To protect the original paper, a blueprint of the drawing was bounced back and forth between them for changes and revisions. After the engineers decided the final design, the draftsmen executed its final drawing. Sometimes, for rush jobs, there was no time to wait for the printer to make a blueprint, so like the male engineers, I developed the habit of making my comments on the original drawings using a soft-lead pencil. This did not sit well with Fred. One day he decided to break me in, teach me good work habits. He returned a drawing to me with a handwritten note telling me "to erase your doodles." I thought, then laughed secretly. I returned it with my own note telling him I'd erase my doodles the same day he orders the male engineers to erase theirs. If he couldn't tell them, he shouldn't tell me, either. In the meantime, he could do it himself or ask a lower draftsman to do it.

From the corner of my eye I saw Fred shake his head before walking to a draftsman. I knew I had won; it had been easier than I had expected. Maybe this would be a good time to push!

The hostile mood of the drafters permeated the plans. I had caught them intentionally showing a fire hydrant connected to a sanitary sewer; or assigning the wrong street for an extensive pavement removal; or writing wrong pipe sizes. These would have caused me deep embarrassment, or even my job, had I not caught them. The drafters' obvious goal was to encircle me with a wagon train of discouragement and then to destroy my career. The spirit of the old west still lived—only this time not for protection but for destruction. But I shielded myself from disasters by striving to keep myself one step ahead of everyone. I plowed through each drawing thoroughly with a fine-toothed comb, as if I was seeking an explosive in a beautifully wrapped package.

It took a while before the resentment of the drafters subsided. Those who could not accept me transferred to other jobs or quit employment and went back to school. Those who stayed, mellowed, and resigned themselves to the fact that I was a supervisor to be reckoned with.

However, as old problems went, new ones came. Among these new faces, Joseph Le Pore, posed the most vigorous challenge to my inner strength. A stubby Hispanic, Joseph carried himself with a swaggering indolence and measured people with the cool arrogance of self-appointed authority. The kind weak people cowered to, he cursed women and intimidated anybody who displeased him. He was a man of marginal qualifications whose only passport to the drafting trade was a semester in a vocational school.

One day, Frank attended a conference out of town and left me temporarily in charge of the drafting room. Joseph grabbed the opportunity to blast the gate to hell. He would show the drafters it was he who could deliver the knockout blow to my career. I had feared this moment would rear its ugly head for a long time.

I had prepared sketches for distribution to the draftsmen. As I stacked the prints, I silently appreciated Frank's arrangement regarding Fred; how good it had been for me. Work flowed back and forth between the drafters through Fred, whose gentle manners went over well with them, especially the women. When asked for help with work problems, he had a way of imparting knowledge without making the other person feel inadequate. He did not evoke adverse reaction from the draftsmen perhaps because they could relate to him in education, race, language, age or sex. For the mutual gentleness between him and them, Fred served as the soft cushion between the drafters' hostilities and myself. Then I froze when the whole scary truth dawned on me. Fred was absent! I must deal with the drafters directly. A torrent of thoughts about Joseph warned me that a strong hurricane was approaching. I could feel it in my bones. Reluctantly, I went around from drafting table to drafting table, distributing sketches. I had barely handed a sheet to Joseph when his shouts startled me.

"What kind of a goddamned sketch is this? Even a dumb eighth grader can do better than this!" His voice thundered across the room.

A paralyzing humiliation gripped me. Helplessly, I watched Joseph shred my sketch, his eyes glistening with excitement as he proudly glanced at the rest of the stunned draftspersons. To top this act, he tossed the shredded pieces of paper at my feet.

A big lump leaped to my throat; my knees weakened. I walked slowly to the window and there I stood looking out, fighting back tears. For the difficulty of containing my emotion, my body shook uncontrollably. But in the meantime, my mind was churning, figuring out how I could come out of this situation with grace and dignity. My future as a supervisor hung on the balance once more. My next move would be critical. I threw a quick glance at the drafters. They seemed delighted, or were they? I felt deserted in the deafeningly quiet room. The crisis lasted for only a few minutes but it seemed forever. As soon as my body stopped convulsing, I told myself not to utter a word, fall apart, yell, or scream. I walked towards my table, a sea of eyes drowning me amidst the suspicious silence. I packed my purse then calmly marched out of the office for the day although it was only three o'clock.

I hopped on the first bus that stopped in front of me without looking at the signboard. I did not care where it was going. As soon as I sat down, the hot tears I had so valiantly held back poured from my eyes. I sobbed, feeling unexpected depths of self-pity. I blew my nose with a tremendous flattening blast that startled the passenger beside me.

"Are you okay, honey?" a female voice asked worriedly.

I acknowledged the words of the sympathizer by looking at her. An old skinny woman clutching a paper sack filled with used clothes, she could not possibly relate to my problem. I thought it best not to say a word to her beyond "I'm okay, thank you" and to just quietly ride the bus round-trip while I sorted out my next move. Questions and answers raced frantically in my mind. Quit the job? And then what? Quit engineering altogether? Surely my feelings were hurt. That was one thing. And then it was entirely another thing to simply flee from the scene just because my feelings were hurt. I had so much invested in engineering—physical, emotional, and financial—that I could not easily give it up because one draftsman inflicted an emotional wound. Oh, no. Noooo resignations. Noooobody will get the satisfaction of seeing me quit. It was inevitable to stand up to the rapid fire of life's machine guns sooner or later. Why not now? A rush of self-indulgence overwhelmed me and I whimpered once more.

The bus driver glanced at me through the rear view mirror to check things out. His eyes heavy on me, I stiffened, wiped my tears and looked away and continued to ransack my brains for the best positive step to take. Those American draftsmen might not be bad beasts after all. Even if they were barbaric, they could surely be tamed if I introduced a few training tactics.

At the end of the ride of stormy tears, I rose like a phoenix and wiped out every trace of emotions. Squaring my shoulders in front of the bus door, I decided I'd write down the incident for Hensch to act on. When the bus stopped in front of City Hall once more, I got off and waited for the correct bus that would take me home.

That night I toiled over the memorandum to Hensch, as though my whole life depended on it. Very coolly and carefully, I detailed the incident in damning detail, blow by blow, explaining things just as they were, without ranting. I made sure no telltale signs of the emotions that had racked me in the bus showed. In conclusion, I recommended disciplinary action against Joseph Le Pore for conduct unbecoming of a city employee, to serve as deterrent to other city employees. I carefully screened the letter for misspellings and replaced weak words with effective ones, which I had plucked from the YWCA's dictionary. Just when I thought it was time to dot the i's and cross the t's, I remembered something very important: the clincher, the one last statement that would evoke a response from the recipient concerning his plan of action, and thus assuring me my efforts had not been in vain. Pleased with the letter's final form, I lay myself to sleep. But I stared at the ceiling a good part of the evening. Anxiety gripped me as unpleasant thoughts crowded my mind. How would Joseph and the other drafters treat me tomorrow? What if Hensch reacted adversely to it? Then the endless picture of myself suppressing tears in the drafting room kept flashing back. And I tossed and turned miserably to shake it off.

First thing the following morning I delivered the letter. With the document in Hensch's warm hands, he had no choice but to act on it, one way or another. I walked out of his office standing tall, flooded with a strange sense of power.

I did not encounter Joseph again until later in the morning in the drafting room when he leered at me in a very triumphant manner. I stiffened myself and avoided him like a mad dog. When I cut a swath across the drafting room, I felt the same twenty pairs of eyes following my face again. From the corner of my eye, I saw Joseph turn to the drafters, a grin plastered across his face. He waved his hands, his fingers forming the letter V for victory.

Joseph did not savor his victory for a long time. At the end of an independent investigation launched by my letter, Hensch reprimanded Le Pore in writing, warning him to stay at his work station at all times, and that any repeat of misconduct toward a fellow employee would be ground for his dismissal.

Each memorandum concerning personnel action was supposed to be confidential, but Hensch's secretary who typed his and the clerk whom I had appreciated with a lunch of tacos and enchiladas to type mine, meshed each other's secrets and sent sparks of gossip flying all over the drafting room.

Joseph smarted at first from his bruised ego, but soon, he could no longer live with the excruciating pain of a wounded machismo. He resigned his job and was not heard from again.

The Joseph Le Pore affair sent a wave of fear through the aisles of the drafting room. The draftsmen began to absorb the idea that I knew how to rise from the dead and strike back. When they saw other draftsmen eventually fired or transferred, or resigned after a collision with me, they viewed me as a formidable woman who was determined to bend anyone who got in my way. Soon, a hissing of murmurs filled the drafting room again. Alleging that their very existence hinged on my whims and caprices, the drafters voted for representation by a labor union. But even the union failed to intimidate me. When I pursued one insubordinate draftsman, my solid documentation of the case helped me crash the massive protective wall erected by the labor union. And I nabbed my bounty.

The citizens also dealt me some trials and tribulations. They refused to talk to me on the telephone upon hearing my voice and accent. They insisted on a male engineer. Hostility was worse in person. On one occasion, there had been a serious flooding. With a draftswoman in tow to attest that I was an engineer, I knocked on the door of a man who had earlier asked to see a city engineer about the problem. A bent old man opened the door. In a growl, he asked us what we came for.

"We came to respond to your complaint, to see the flooding problem you have here. I am an engineer," I said in a voice so deliberately low he had to crane his neck to hear me. I had learned from experience nothing worked as well as soothing, calculated tones to calm anger and bring people to reason. But even this strategy failed.

The man cocked his head and sized me up with such brutal certainty as a person unworthy of his time. "You don't know nothing!" he grunted disgustedly and slammed the door on my face.

Stunned, with my nose only a few inches from the surface of a closed door, I turned around and walked towards the car, the draftswoman following me in silence.

"I don't think the old boy is crazy about me," I deadpanned to the draftswoman while we were fastening our seatbelts. I peeped at the side mirror to check my face.

She threw her head back in laughter. "Great gobs of goose grease?" she exclaimed. "How the devil can you put up with all these problems?"

"Easy," I said. "I just don't let them get to me." But in my deepest core, I fervently wished life would get easier.

# Chapter 13

# The Bottom of the Ladder, Part 2

The drafting room could be reached through either of two entryways. A door, the one to my right as I came out of the elevator, was accessible to citizens seeking information on sewer stub-outs, street widths, and locations of existing waterlines. The citizens, who might be plumbers, engineers in private practice, builders, or just ordinary taxpayers, filled the small space between the door and a counter tended by an employee between the hours of eight and five o'clock. I chose the indirect entry to the drafting room—only employees knew about this—through a door in front of the elevator. Debbie Thompson smiled courteously behind her desk, the barrier and screening area, as she spoke on the telephone. She was young, blond, and green-eyed and had a clear eager face. "Mr. Bailey? Of course, one moment please. May I tell him who's calling?"

Hearing Debbie, I paused. When she placed the telephone back on its cradle, I remarked, "I did not know you screened calls. That's a good idea."

"Only for engineers," Debbie muttered while nonchalantly turning the pages of the telephone directory.

"What about me? I'm also all engineer. Screen my calls, too, will you?" I said, excitedly. "That way you can help me avoid mean citizens."

Debbie shrugged her shoulders. Noticing her lack of enthusiasm about my suggestion, I decided not to push the issue; it was not that important. I proceeded to my little corner in the drafting room. I worked in silence for a while, then for some unknown reason, Bob Blair entered my mind. It had been almost year since he led me to the drafting room. We had smiled at each other occasionally here and

111

there, but we had never really sat down to talk. I wondered how he was doing. The thought wouldn't leave me, so I stood up and walked to his private office.

Bob leaned over a large contour map of a new housing subdivision, his trembling hand toying with a compass. He motioned for me to sit down on the chair in front of his desk. I asked how he was and he said he was fine. "But I don't understand it," he said unintelligibly. "I have had my soil testing laboratory for years, and now Hensch wants me to resign because of conflict of interest."

I had no idea what he was talking about, but I felt a twinge of pity for Bob because of his worsening muscular disease. I was almost sure his health, more than anything else, prompted Hensch to let him go. Lately, Bob's handwriting had become illegible, his motor movements too slow to accomplish a quarter of a day's work. He had aged shockingly the last few months. I looked out of the window and watched workers wearing orange vests and hard hats place barricades on the street below. An imposing crane stood nearby. Another road reconstruction was about to start in the heart of downtown. We conversed some more about our jobs and the common problems we ran into regularly. To my surprise and delight, I found out we did the same kind of work which included design of streets, waterlines, and drainage and sanitary sewer systems and other duties as assigned by Frank. When I returned to my desk, I was agitated by mixed feelings— sadness for a good man ravaged by a cruel disease, joy over an impending promotional opportunity and guilt over such joy. Then, there was the aggravation at the prospect of fighting Hensch for this promotion, because he himself was a formidable person who would go to any extent to get his way.

In his early fifties, Erwin Hensch still rated as good-looking. His light brown hair graying swiftly at the sides highlighted a stern face. His tall stature, erect posture, and dark suits exuded an air of distinction; something he tried at all cost to accomplish. It was part of the act of being the Director of Public Works of the premier city in New Mexico. When he spoke, he squared his shoulders, a warning that something important was going to come out of his tight, thin lips. Everybody better listen. He talked frequently of Minnesota where many Germans, his lineage, settled from Europe. "Us Germans" often opened his statements. He ran the department ruthlessly, like his own empire, aiming only to please the City Manager who had the power to hire and fire directors. Whatever Hensch ordered, his seven division chiefs obeyed like trained puppies. Occasionally, he dropped in the drafting room, unannounced, to survey quietly this part of his kingdom. He evoked furtive glances from the drafters to whom his presence was easily intimidating.

## Don't Ever Tell Me You Can't

During my first few months in the department, Hensch was highly involved with the American Public Works Association. He automatically drafted all the male engineers in the association, paid their dues from his office budget, and invited them to all its functions. He left me out. I ignored Hensch's inequity, just like Debbie's, because I had learned to select my battles. It was better to ignore nips and save my energies to fight big bites that could swallow up my existence.

Almost from our initial meeting, I had formed an instinctive suspicion of Hensch's exaggerated self-importance and arrogance. Now that suspicion was narrowing into downright repugnance. It seemed as if he was deliberately being as abrasive as possible. There had been his unguarded statements like the time he praised an American Indian employee. "He's so smart, you wouldn't think he's Indian." Or the time he told me he "refused a Singaporean boy in my home because I had two daughters and the world is so mixed as it is." Several off-the-cuff remarks showed his hidden biases concerning inferiority and superiority among humans. I had parried those unpleasant remarks, although I resented them. My instinct cautioned me that he was intentionally intimidating me or subtly reminding me about my proper place in American society as he perceived it. He was entitled to his strategy but I had no intention of abetting it. And that bothered me. The more thoughts I gathered about Hensch, the farther the possibility of getting Bob's job seemed to become. The mere idea of facing Hensch about the promotion pulled an instinctive rumbling groan from the pit of my stomach.

But I wanted Bob's job! I must have it because I was qualified, even more so now with my discovery that I had been doing the very same kind of work. I couldn't let an opportunity like this pass without a shred of gut.

I hurried to Frank. He was Bob's supervisor; therefore, he had the power to choose Blair's replacement. He could save me from the horror of facing Hensch. Wasting no time, I poured out my sentiments to Frank in his office.

"I'd give it to you," Frank said, rolling a short pencil between his teeth, "but you know there are two guys above me: Bill Stevens and Erwin Hensch. Go talk to them yourself. See if you can convince them to promote you."

Frank took the path of the least resistance, I thought, but that was his prerogative. I rushed to Bill Stevens, as though my problem was more crucial than a collapsed bridge or burst pipe. The same story came tumbling down from my mouth.

An elephant of a man, City Engineer Bill Stevens became a successful professional despite his severe stutter. With his speech problem, I imagined he had to climb a few walls himself to get where he was. I supposed he would help me avoid talking with Hensch. But he was deeply entrenched in bureaucracy and the politics of city government, which had stripped him of decisiveness. He sympathized with me but he also took the scenic route and pointed me to Hensch for a decision. Tossed back to square one, I wondered how Hensch was going to react. Or more than anything else, *how I would react.* Already I felt uneasy just thinking of the prospect of the confrontation with a man who, in more ways than one, had implied to me that he was a child of a greater god. I supposed as a female engineer from a foreign country, I would grow used to asserting myself to men of his kind, but at the moment it was still new and rather frightening.

I went on to see Hensch. I explained to him how I sought to advance myself, how an engineer's knowledge could be expanded and the city's organization enhanced, how I had been doing the same job as Bob Blair's, and how much money he would save if he did not have to train a new employee. But none of these could be done without his approval.

He stopped me dead on my tracks.

"I understand everything you're saying, but you are not a registered engineer in this country. Your registration in the Philippines does not count here. I can't promote you until you have your local registration."

Hensch's words shot through me like a poisoned arrow and painfully settled the issue. I was a wounded animal, my enthusiasm for my pursuit flickering out. I could not be promoted at the time; I lacked a requirement. Reluctantly, I let my trophy go. But I told him I'd try again next time a position of similar nature opened up, that I'd be making sure I possessed all the requirements, definitely including the registration with the New Mexico board of professional engineers. It could be arranged; I felt positive about it.

With that pleasant exchange, Hensch and I headed on our separate paths. He proceeded to hire a white man to fill Blair's position and I went on to pursue my local registration. I invested a whopping $70 on a set of review books, and studied away at night, confident that in the near future, my status as an engineer would be better, much better, if I summoned the strength to continue on the course I had charted.

෨෮෫෨෮෫෨෮෫

I was sitting on the couch in front of Mrs. Hutton's office, waiting for Tom to pick me up for one of our dinner splurges. I had looked forward to this evening, like all our nights out, although I could not plan on eating anything heavy. It had only been a week since I had my gum operation in a hospital. The sharp piercing pain had been gone for two days now, but nevertheless, liquid diet was still the order of the day, and for another week yet. Then why all this warm feeling of anticipation? It was the company, I reflected, and not the dining that made each of our dates an occasion.

When Tom walked in the door, his eyes had a special glow. "The divorce is final," he exulted. "We'll get married tomorrow." After the initial embrace, he pulled his head backward to examine me from a longer distance. He frowned at what he considered a plunging neckline. He fastened the next upper button of my dress.

"Tomorrow?" My eyebrows arched up in disbelief. I smiled and showed him the dental packing that covered all my teeth. "Are you sure?"

"Tomorrow," he countered with a positive nod.

After I promised Mrs. Hutton to be back before the curfew hour, Tom, his hand lightly on my back, guided me to the door, then out into his cream Dodge Dart. He started the engine and with a roar, we were on our way. It was the basic car, its dashboard displaying only the operator's basic gauges. I thought that if we did get married, this would be our car. I'd be driving it. But first I must learn how to drive. Then marriage dawned on me. It just came home to me now that marriage was not such an enormous decision to make, after all. Tom wanted us to get married tomorrow. I wanted to suggest that we should wait at least two more weeks until the periodontist removed the packing in my mouth. But he had already decided: tomorrow. Any reason for delaying the marriage was trivial.

Now it was my turn to think and decide, but I felt like I had given it a lot of thought already and there was nothing left to ponder. It seemed like all we really needed was the official marriage contract, the piece of paper, that would cement our arrangement and erase the shadow of guilt that had hounded me after every intimate second I spent with Tom.

"Yes!" It was now my turn to exult. "Let's get married tomorrow." And circled my arm around his shoulders.

The following day I took a day off and Tom and I were married in a civil ceremony in Estancia, a small town outside Albuquerque. Tom described me as a "blushing bride" in my long-sleeved, knee-length dress the color of strawberry ice cream, while I thought he looked dapper in his charcoal suit, white shirt, and gray tie with diagonal cream thin stripes.

With the marriage ceremony behind us, Tom, our two witnesses, and I trooped to the same hotel that was the scene of our first meeting since Manila. In its dimly lit restaurant, my companions dined on thick slabs of juicy steaks, baked potatoes and the works, while I sipped through a straw, a cup of bouillon. At the end of the meal, our witnesses raised their wineglasses to toast our new life together. "To happiness!" they proclaimed and we repeated the words while clinking our wineglasses against theirs. With that, the dinner formally ended and the wedding party of four dispersed.

I snuggled towards the warmth of Tom's body inside the car. He placed his right arm around my shoulders and steered the car with his left hand, away from the parking lot. I was silent, twisting the ring Tom had placed upon my finger earlier. The recitation of vows still echoed in my ear. It was solemn. It touched my soul. Drugged by this cleansed feeling, I gleaned at the past, searching for youthful dreams I could compare with the present reality. Finding none, the futile exercise brought a smile to my face. All those years, I had been so busy pursuing an odd career and fighting for survival that I had not given an iota of thought to the type of wedding I'd like to have when I grew up. Here I was now, a legitimately married woman.

"What are you thinking about?" Tom asked, pulling me closer to him.

Forced to attention, I looked up and noticed our car parked in front of Mike's apartment.

"What are we doing here?" I asked my face at him.

"We will tell Mike the news," he declared.

We! I had no more desire to let his brother in on what I had decided to do in my life, let alone get him up in the middle of the night just to tell him the news. Fear of Mike's adverse reaction shot through me.

We found Mike in bed, asleep, covered to his neck in sheets. Tom shook him by the shoulder. Opening his eyes and seeing Tom's face only, Mike smiled at the pleasant surprise.

"Hey Tommy, what's happening, man?" he asked, half-dazed.

"Celia and I got married," Tom answered, happily. "I thought you might want to give us your best wishes."

Tom's words jolted Mike to attention. He turned his head, and when his eyes found me, his face hardened.

"I don't give a damn whether you got married or not." And words of fury spewed uncontrollably out of his mouth. He plopped himself to bed, turned his back on us, and pulled the sheets to the tip of his head. The sheets muffled his voice but the theme was the same: hatred for his brother's marriage to me and fury for having been disturbed from sleep for such insignificant event.

With Mike's sputtering of anger, Tom marched out of the apartment. I followed him and slammed the door behind me.

Silence fell between Tom and me in the car.

I was quite surprised to find myself neither bleeding from nor infuriated by Mike's verbal assault. It was as if nothing happened. What difference did his opinion make at this point? After I had been shocked the first time I heard his tirade about racial supremacy when he was our roommate, I had learned to gradually tune his opinions out, until finally like a while ago, they did not matter anymore. His words had simply bounced, like water off a duck's back. Perhaps that was all life was, one long tuning-out process.

The situation was evidently painful to Tom. I glanced at his face as he managed the steering wheel. His jaws were clenched and there was hurt in his eyes. Still freshly subdued by the calming effect of the vow "to love, cherish, and obey my husband," I did not blame him

"Well," I laughed, "so much for brotherly love!"

He smiled and shook his head. It was almost midnight when we reached the little house he had rented for us.

The following day, I was stripped of every shade of fear of eviction from my cubbyhole. I excitedly checked out of the YWCA. I told the lady caretakers I was moving out to an apartment. Mrs. Hutton insisted on getting my parents' address and telephone number so she could unload her responsibility for me.

"Don't worry about me. I just got married. I'm twenty-seven years old, a civil engineer, and my parents live in the Philippines," I said.

Mrs. Hutton's jaw dropped to her waist.

Tom and I moved to our new nest: a one-room squat square adobe house in the valley, several blocks away from the muddy Rio Grande. We thought the little box of a hut was a bargain at sixty-five dollars monthly rent including all utilities. It would be peaceful and quiet, too, since it was located behind a slightly bigger adobe house that abutted the street. A narrow dirt alley provided the access between our house and the street. A public library and bigger houses of the same character completed the neighborhood picture.

I gazed about our new house. Immediately, I checked the bathroom out. My long history of restroom discomfort always caused me to be sucked like a tornado by bathrooms and toilets. When I stepped on the floor of the prefabricated shower stall unit, it gave slightly. After I pulled the plastic curtain and enclosed myself in the cubicle, ecstasy bathed my whole being. Here was privacy one more time. I stepped down and out past the commode, into the main room of the house, and noticed the walls had been spruced up. It still smelled of fresh paint. Light blue. A queen-size bed, covered with white spread of fringed lumpy cotton material, dominated the room. A couple of feet away, stood a small oval wooden table, the kind that shrunk into a smaller square one when the hinged outer leaves were allowed to fall.

117

I sat on one of the two chairs and ran my fingers to feel the smooth shiny finish of the table. I glanced around. There were the normal perks of refrigerator and sink and stove, otherwise that was it. Our little house on the desert.

Initially, marriage seemed to offer a different kind of joy than another kind I had experienced when I accomplished something, like when I received my engineer's diploma or my professional registration, or my American visa, or being ecstatic, dancing around and exuberant. Marriage was a quiet joy generated by a feeling of being valued by a man and giving to him a part of myself.

But I did not realize that this same marriage contained venom potently dangerous to my non-traditional career when hints of trouble surfaced—a husband's excessive jealousy and unreasonable possessiveness. These might have appeared during our courtship but they had been fleeting then and easily unnoticed. Suddenly, now, they were blocking the view to my goal. This new stumbling block became evident when Tom started to call me at work with alarming frequency. And then, at home, he cross-examined me regarding my whereabouts during the past ten hours, whom I ate lunch with and where, what conversations I had with whom and how. The tone of his voice and the glint of suspicion in his eyes implied that the men I worked with were intruding in some private territory, some space he owned, and did not want anyone else there.

The daily ritual of making myself available to answer the phone eventually snapped me.

"This is the third time I called. Where have you been?"

The anger, which had been building up inside me, exploded, and I snarled a heated answer: "I don't sit around here all day waiting for you to call!"

More problems surfaced. One time we attended a party thrown by one of his co-workers. I noticed that in America, a couple's togetherness in a party ended as soon as they entered the door. The men trooped to the backyard while the women congregated at the kitchen. I suppose in the course of our education about life in general, we miss out entirely on some important lessons. In my case, I had not learned about women, especially married ones. My world had been populated with men, mostly engineers, architects, draftsmen, and construction suppliers. Of course, there had been Mother and my sisters who had touched my life intimately in the pursuit of my profession. There had been the workplace secretaries who had something to do with my job. But they were different. They talked about livelihood. Then there had been the YWCA girls but contact with them had been limited to silly giggles. Outside of them, I regarded other women as simply that—people who were not men. It came as a complete surprise to me then that there were housewives and mothers in this world and they talked about subjects such as children, day-care centers, weight problems, and recipes.

I listened to the women for a while and, not being able to contribute to topics to which I could not relate, I slipped out to the patio to join the men's conversation. It turned out to be a move that would spell trouble with big capital letters. All the while I was conversing with the men about jobs, business, and current events, I could feel Tom's eyes focused on me intensely, making me feel somewhat unclean. On the way home, Tom lowered the boom on me.

"This flirting with men must stop!" he said, his face stern.

"Ah!" Light dawned. "Is that what those baleful glances were all about?" I probed, staring at him and waiting for an answer.

"At family parties in this country, wives socialize with wives and husbands with husbands," he said. "You spent most of the time flirting with the men."

"I beg your pardon," I said, indignantly. "That wasn't flirting."

"You were laughing and carrying on!" He was angry.

But it was an anger that was tough to respond to because I knew it covered a multitude of things. Something had been bothering him—my association with men at the party and at my place of work.

"I am comfortable around men. I went to school with men and I have been working with men as far back as I can remember. I have adapted to men in an arrangement that doesn't seem to be acceptable in this society or any other. Why can't a man and a woman be friends or work together, or even just carry on a conversation, much like two men or two women? Why should there be suspicions that something beyond friendship or business is going on? Men, to me, are like women, except that they are men. I find it easy to converse with men and quite frankly, I don't see anything wrong with it." I wondered if I made sense to him.

Tom spoke emphatically. "You are my wife now."

I frantically offered some more explanation to try to make sense, to make him understand. But he didn't, wouldn't, or couldn't, and he frustrated me to tears.

Other social gatherings followed. In order to save the fragile marriage, I limited my circulation around the wives when the party was sponsored by his work place. But after an office function sponsored by my office, we argued viciously again about the men on the drive home.

"I work with men. I have to deal with them," I insisted. "There's nothing wrong with talking to them. You must trust me. It's the engineer in me talking to them."

"But you are my wife, too, I don't care," he said, adamantly.

"You have to care," I snapped back. "You knew all along I am an engineer. It was not like I received my diploma yesterday and you are shocked today. Before I came to the United States, you even asked me if I was good at it."

This time, I had a sneaking suspicion that my husband, the person who I thought would be the solution to my problem was now becoming, at breakneck speed, a big part of the problem.

# Chapter 14

# The First Rung

On the brighter side, Tom was very thoughtful. He brought me a grapefruit at work every morning. He showered me with fresh bouquets of flowers almost every other week. The accompanying card always read "From your loving stranger." I always ran my fingers lightly on the flowers, feeling their soft petals, their damp green leaves. They had life despite having been cut off from their natural habitat in some hothouse, where they had been nurtured with tender loving care. For a price, the grower had snipped these twelve long stems, each holding a perfect rosebud. Someone had arranged it attractively for a buyer who wanted to bring sunshine to another person's life. Tom wanted to make me happy. However, for a pragmatic person like me who had grown up in a place where spending money on flowers was unheard of, the flowers moved but saddened me. I would run my fingers on the thorny stems. I'd think, in three or four days, the flowers would lose their gloss and suppleness. Their leaves would dry up and turn brittle. In a week, they would wilt totally. Deader than hell, that's the ultimate fate of these poor, lovely flowers. When I picked them up and tossed them for their funeral in the trash can, I'd get the same familiar feeling that the money used for its purchase—half of which was mine—might as well have been wasted, too. I shook my head. Weighed down by this pragmatism, I dreaded once more the idea of having to thank Tom, who in all honesty, just meant to brighten my day.

"Your loving stranger." That said it all. Tom and I barely knew each other, really, when we got married. Miles separated us when it came to experience, education, beliefs, upbringing, culture, sociological behavior, preferences and just about everything else. The glaring, acute differences in our pathetic combination became evident. Tom was romantic, I was pragmatic. He kept a small, familiar, and comfortable circle of friends. I loved meeting new people. He accused me of being selfish. I pronounced him guilty of altruism, the root of all evils. He had grown up in logging camps where men were king. I had come from a family where women ruled. His upbringing left him fraught with doubts about himself. My self-confidence bordered on haughtiness. His parents had trained him to be fiercely protective of his brothers and sister. My parents had taught me to be self-sufficient, not dependent on the family men for anything. His father had given him no emphasis on education. My father had encouraged me to be a professional. Tom had attended the seminary and almost became a Catholic priest. I had questioned religion at age eight. He wanted a traditional wife out of me. I was nowhere close to being one. I wanted to please him first. He pleased his father first, then mother, followed by brothers and sister, relatives, friends, then me—dead last in the pecking order. I considered him an individual with individual needs. He considered me a part of him and wanted me defined by him. He drank beer, lots of beer, and told me right from the get go to get used to it. He's not alcoholic, he assured me. "So don't even think of changing me." And yet he wanted to change me. He wanted to change the way I dressed, the way I acted and reacted, the way I spoke. He even seriously considered sending me to a finishing school! While he never attacked me verbally in public, I felt he did dislike me intensely and did not respect me.

Our long, sizzling letters in between short visits in the Philippines had given Tom and me mere peeks into each other's personalities. I remember how many times I had tried to probe his mind, to see how much I could sway him. One time, while we were having cocktails, I had tried to pick his brains. I asked him how long he had been in the Air Force. He said eight years and talked at length about all the employment benefits. I asked if he was being used to his fullest potential. He had frowned thoughtfully and did not answer. I seized the opportunity to recount my early struggles as an engineer up to the point where I left my government job to work for H. R. Lopez & Company.

"My government job was secure but the same question haunted me. Was I using myself to my fullest potential?" I said, flattening my two hands on my chest. I had followed it with the question: "Have you thought of going back to college to finish what you started years ago?"

My lecture had been a success. Tom had written his mother and told her he had met this girl who had made him realize he had been goofing off all these years. He did not re-enlist. Instead, he enrolled at the University of New Mexico in search of his "fullest potential." He would have not done so nor even thought of doing so had it not been for me. Yet, I would not be in this town had it not been for him. We were each other's anchors. We needed each other and we were morally obligated to each other. Conscience was the hot glue that fused the disparities of our lives. But the strain of adjusting to our conflicting personalities was tearing us apart. Over and over, we argued heatedly about the way I acted and reacted, how I walked, the clothes I wore, whom I talked to, the words I said. He criticized everything about my disposition, my character, my personality, and me. Every time we drove home from socializing, he would zero in on my immediate past actions and the verbal fight began. I tried to change my ways, hoping that by doing so, his personal attacks on me would stop. I wore clothes that he and his mother bought for me according to their conservative tastes. I was the little rag doll, willing to be dressed for success. At social scenes, I held back my tongue. I simply sat beside him and limited my interaction to a demure smile every now and then. Tom loved the change. He was Ronald Reagan basking in the glory of the loving dutiful gaze of Nancy Reagan. Good for him, but every fiber of my being protested the charade. I was going to discuss it with him. I had hardly begun divulging my secret torment over the new me when the meeting blew up in acrimony. We traded fierce verbal jabs again.

"I take you the way you are. Why can't you take me the way I am?" I asked, which was the long and short of the ongoing conflict. Exchange of words fanned the smoldering fire of his insane jealousy.

"You're acting like you have a boyfriend stashed somewhere," he said frequently with mounting suspicion. Each statement like that followed by long stretches of muted silence from me pushed our marriage closer to the brink of collapse. One time to test his feelings, I offered to give up my career, explaining it was simply not possible for me, a civil engineer, to work in a place without men. But he didn't want me to give up my career, either. He always took pride in introducing me to people, as "my wife, she's a civil engineer." He just couldn't accept the natural circumstances attached to a female civil engineer.

He dropped out of college. Drinking with friends became a nightly affair for him. When I came home from a day of frustration at work, I ate quickly and climbed into an empty bed. I felt so alone in the world. Many times, towards dawn, I lay awake, reviewing the situation. I could see my life stretching out ahead of me, filled with ever-growing unpleasant conflicts. What was the end of it, what was its meaning, or hope?

Then, I'd roll out of bed the next morning tired and defenseless, tortured by the thought that marriage might be another long, drawn-out struggle. If it was, I didn't want any part of it. And yet, for someone who had never learned the art of making easy choices, I was finding it difficult to simply abandon our disintegrating relationship. I kept thinking that I had nothing against him. As long as he kept his fists to his body, I dealt with him, round by round, blow by blow, mentally and verbally.

There were fundamental things we both believed in, notably honesty and integrity. If I could only get him to understand my profession, there would be no suspicions. If I could only make him see that, honestly, a married woman was an entity separate from her husband, and thus, had individual needs not contingent upon his, there would be harmony. If I could only extract from his head the suffocating notion of gender roles, I knew that with caution and diplomacy, I could lead him to my track and married life would be a waltz. There seemed to be no end to the shadows of distraction that my marriage was casting over my career.

ဢ෨ဢ෨ဢ෨

Instead of promoting me, the City hired a new engineer to replace Bob Blair. I looked curiously at the new engineer. He was thirty-five, I figured, and was wearing an elegant pale gray business suit and a wide tie with psychedelic designs of swirling lines of yellow and purple on a sky blue background. He had dark hair that matched a deep tan. "From skiing in Aspen," he volunteered. His other conversation, dropping names of places and people and brands of imported European cars, revealed the air of a man very impressed with himself. To top it all, he showed me his certificate of registration as a professional engineer in New Mexico, mounted in a gold-rimmed frame. That did it for me. I was incensed! If I owned that certificate, it would be me, not him who would have had that job. But I realized I was in a new country and I had to live by the new rules. I must accept that such was life for a new immigrant. Even a tree once uprooted and transplanted to a different soil has to struggle to grab a hold of the new earth in order to survive, and then thrive. The dirt does not adjust; the plant does. That was my case, no doubt about it. I couldn't complain about life's unfairness; I knew I'd have to prove myself. I only wished it would not take so long. And I thought of the infinite haul ahead of me to keep up with the Americans.

The thought galvanized me to a decision to use my solitary confinement in our little shack to good use: to spend the time to dust the cobwebs in my mind and start reviewing engineering examination problems. It was a good place to start the haul.

In the beginning, it was frustrating. After years of absence from the academic environment, my rusty brain squeaked when the motions of studying began. Sometimes when I found myself nodding, half-asleep, I forced myself to pace the dirt alley and get some fresh air to awaken my motivation. Then I returned to the dining table to resume my studies. Before long, however, discipline took command. Every night I managed to channel my marital frustrations to the books of engineering review. Soon, the rhythm of study oiled the squeak out from my brains, and I was solving analytical and theoretical design problems at a smoother pace.

My confidence soared once more. I assured myself I'd pass the examinations, regardless of how long they were. Of all my peculiarities, I had long suspected confidence to be the strongest, and it was a defect. It had gotten me in troubles. I had fought it, yet it always came back, stronger than ever, seemingly indestructible. Armed with this confidence, I wrote to the State Board of Registration for Professional Engineers and asked for the details of their next scheduled examination. The Board responded favorably by sending me forms and booklets of rules and regulations and sample questions from previous examinations.

The Board's positive reply propelled me to greater heights of optimism. And I studied and studied and studied. One day, I received a letter from the board, scheduling me for an oral examination and interview to determine if I would be allowed to take the written examination. I took the board's invitation very seriously. Although the board did not ask me to, I prepared to bring every conceivable evidence of my professional education, background and experience, including transcripts of records, diploma, résumé, prints of plans that showed my design, and specification books that I had authored. Mother had always said, the guy who is well prepared beats the guy who works like a carabao.

Tom drove me to Santa Fe for that unforgettable event, my face-to-face meeting with the men who controlled the practice of engineering in the state of New Mexico—The Board. While he waited in the parking lot, five men with shocks of graying hair, in business suits, sat around a rectangular wood-laminated table in the conference room, waiting to grill me.

Upon their offer, I sat on an empty chair that they had provided for me. When I glanced around, I noticed a filing cabinet and bookshelves against a wall were the only other furnishings in the room. A frail woman with coarse skin and a nose a trifle large, the secretary of the board, set the tape recorder for the proceedings. Taking note of the men in their suits, I mentally recalled the image of myself on the mirror the last time I had looked before I hopped in the car, to check if my physical appearance measured up to theirs. My hair, which hung loosely on my back, was pitch black against my sleeveless apple-green dress, which had a simple round high neckline. No facial make-up save for a hint of burnt mocha lipstick. Finding no point of comparison between the men's appearance and mine, I resigned myself to the fact that this was it. I ran my forefingers from the outer corners of my eyes to the back of my ears, and when I was sure I had swept every lock of hair away from my face, I nodded with a smile at the gentlemen around me. I was ready to take them on.

The men introduced themselves and without beating around the bush, got right smack down to business. One by one they asked questions that ranged from practical to technical, from my educational background to my board examination experience to my exposure in the work arena. They gauged my ability to think on my feet and asked my opinions on certain employer-employee relation problems and on professional ethics. Satisfied that they had covered every possible facet of the board requirements, the five men told me through the chairman, to please step out and wait outside the room while they deliberated on my fate behind closed doors.

"We will determine if you are qualified to take the next scheduled examination. We'll call you in again and let you know, one way or the other about our decision," concluded the chairman, an intimidating figure with broad shoulders and a penetrating stare.

I stepped out as told and began to feel the tension that I had camouflaged so well behind my controlled, studied calm during the interview. More nervous than a whore in church now while I left my fate in the hands of five men, I paced the hall. As I burnt a path in the middle of the corridor, the men's questions and my answers kept flooding my mind. I kept convincing myself I had projected whatever the men wanted to hear and see. But had I really? Should I have said something else? When they had asked why I spent only ten years of elementary and high school education while they did twelve years, and I had answered "I don't know why you need twelve years. I studied your language but you did not study mine; I studied your full history but you did not study mine. I studied all the other courses you studied. I really don't know why you went to school two more years." A wave of laughter had inundated the men and they had unanimously agreed that perhaps they had too many basket-weaving courses. Had I said the right thing or had I made the men feel inadequate? Would they strike back and declare they won't allow me to take the next examination for some reason or another? That would certainly set me back a few years before I could compete with the men in City Hall. On the other hand, if they decided to allow me to take the examination, a tougher, more intense preparation laid ahead. Either decision would not ease my life. Back and forth I paced and, on and on, my mind churned out a mixture of optimism, pessimism, misgivings, hopes, until the secretary's voice telling me to re-enter the room broke my train of thoughts.

After I sat down, I noticed the men, who earlier had looked stern, were now wearing smiles on their faces. As it turned out, the Board agreed unanimously that they would waive the written examination requirement in my case. They said my credentials measured up to the State's standards for professional engineers, therefore, they would register me as a professional engineer in New Mexico on the basis of my registration in the Philippines.

"You might be pleased to know," the chairman also announced, "that you are the first and only foreign national we have ever accepted for registration on the basis of reciprocating registration in another country. In the past we have rejected some Israelis, Germans, Pakistanis, Polish, and Filipinos. We required them to take the engineer-in-training examination and the professional engineer's examination."

When I stepped out of the room for good, I flew to where Tom was and I gushed insufferably. Tom kept saying, "Congratulations, honey," but it was not enough to shut me up. I had to prattle on and spit the excitement out of my system, or I'd explode. Before Tom turned on the ignition key, we decided to celebrate my New Mexico registration by taking the long scenic route to Albuquerque. As he quietly managed the winding road on the slope of the Sandia Mountains, I continued to exult about the new milestone of my career, how I knew all along that I could make it happen, but that I had not expected it to be that easy. I talked about a letter I'd write Father so he could take another trip to his hometown and brag about his daughter, *the registered professional engineer in America.* Drugged by the delight of a fresh achievement, I talked incessantly. All Tom said periodically was "I'm proud of you, honey."

We dropped by our friends who lived in the mountains and shared the good news with them. We raised mugs of home brew until late into the night.

When I received my certificate of registration one week later, I raced to Hensch's office to flaunt the piece of document to him. Hensch's office was the choicest spot on the fourth floor where one could look down and see a bird's eye view of downtown Albuquerque. Located at the end of the hall, it generated little or no traffic, just like a house on a cul-de-sac. Whatever visitors it generated, he fully expected them because they had to get appointment dates and hours through his secretary. With my honest exhilaration over my latest achievement, I had convinced his secretary, a sweet motherly woman, to let me in without prior appointment.

Hensch was sitting on his executive swivel chair, his fingers tapping thoughtfully on the surface of his desk, where he had been reading and signing various public works contracts. He raised his face, surprised that I had come in without warning.

"The Board registered me," I exclaimed, happily, and I laid the certificate flat on his desk. The wording was very readable from his seat. Celia Tomlinson, Professional Engineer Number 4895." What do you think of that? Isn't that neat?"

Hensch frowned. He bit his lip and thought for a minute. "Congratulations," he said. His hands stayed on the documents on the desk.

"Thank you," I answered, and stood erect. My hands were laid flat on the thick transparent glass that covered his desktop.

A chilly standoff divided us. Hensch focused his stare on the pile of paperwork while I stayed glued to the front edge of his desk, my eyes boring into the top of his head. I watched him turn page after page of standard contract forms. Sensing the air in his room had not moved, he looked up, eyebrows raised.

"Congratulations, I said." he repeated, and removed his eyeglasses and placed them on the desk beside the papers.

"Thank you, again." I acknowledged, and shifted my weight from left foot to right foot.

"Well?" he asked. His hands flew up in the air, palms up.

"Well? Congratulations, is that all? Aren't you going to make some adjustments? I'm a registered professional engineer now in this country, like the men, you know," I said, and crossed my arms under my chest. "I understand every engineer here got his position upgraded after he had been registered by the board." And I rattled off the names of the engineers who had received promotions after getting their registration. Hearing and seeing no response, I focused my eyes on a vacant chair, where an expected guest normally sat. I seriously toyed with the idea of planting myself there.

Pushing his swivel chair as far back as it could go, Hensch rolled his eyes toward the ceiling while his head rested on his hands clasped behind his neck. In apparent fear that I might homestead in his office for the remainder of the day, he stood up, emitted a deep breath, walked around his desk, straddled his arm across my shoulders, and then slowly guided me to the door. Out through the hall we walked, then through the door of his administrative assistant. He asked me to take a chair.

"Give her a pay raise," he ordered his assistant, then left hurriedly. When I heard the sound of a slammed door, I knew he was back in his private office. I secretly hoped he did not give his secretary a bad time.

128

The administrative assistant, called "high pockets" for his height of over six-and-a-half feet, hemmed and hawed. He rearranged the top of his desk, moved paperweights here and there, opened and closed drawers, before he stood up and pulled out the forms for certain personnel action from the supply cabinet behind him. He filled out the forms, asking me occasional questions.

"I'll have to give this to a clerk for typing," he said.

"I'll wait here," I said, my hands neatly clasped on my lap.

I left the assistant's office only after I had signed the paperwork for my salary adjustment.

The token raise in pay fell short of my goal of position adjustment similar to the men's prize when they had become registered engineers, but I accepted it without complaint. At least Hensch did not throw a blank refusal at my face. Still, the incident, which barely put a dent on the wall of inequity in my sphere, represented a significant success. It sharpened my resolve to continue hammering at it and to eventually crack it. The edge of my determination to win the fight had just been sharpened anew.

# Chapter 15

❧

# The Second Rung

T om was handling our old cream Dodge Dart steadily, periodically gulping beer from a can. Thick snow blanketed Highway 1-40 again. Snowflakes continued to come down, and the drifts deepened in the vast desert between Arizona and New Mexico. When we reached a stretch that had been snowplowed, Tom stepped on the accelerator for more speed; he had no intention of missing our estimated time of arrival at Fort Defiance, Arizona and worrying his parents. He had always been good at getting us there a couple of hours before the first dinner of our regular weekend-long visit. I had enjoyed the first few trips here, taking in the novelty of the exotic scenarios of gigantic red rocks against a background of red earth and clear blue sky, American Indian men walking on the roadsides, and many pickups overflowing with Navajo squaws dressed in their colorful costumes. In the beginning, I had been awed by fishing through a hole in the ice-covered Bluewater Lake, as well as eating juicy thick slabs of steaks that Clay barbecued for himself, Peggy, Tom, and me. But lately, I was beginning to feel the strain of spending weekend after weekend on this routine.

I was curled into the seat beside Tom. At my feet lay a brown paper sack containing a six-pack of cold beer, which we had purchased from a drive-by liquor store and another sack containing empty cans. It was my duty to stoop down, reach for the beer, and hand it to him, while he drove. He was the pilot, I was the flight attendant, an arrangement we both adapted to. I had been pretty quiet throughout the trip, and usually, since Tom rarely spoke, if I did not talk, there was no conversation. Noticing the peace and quiet, he placed the beer between his thighs, freed his hand, and tenderly squeezed the back of my neck. His hand was ice cold from the beer can. "What are you so quiet about?" he asked. "Say something."

Say something. It was the opening I was hoping for. Without much ado, I spouted out what had been bothering me.

"You want to talk, okay," I said. "Why are we going to Fort Defiance every weekend? I can't grasp the appeal of a three-hundred-mile round trip every weekend to visit in-laws. I can think of five hundred things a couple can do on Saturdays and Sundays other than visit in-laws."

He assured me, "If I didn't have to deliver machinery parts to Dad, we won't be coming to Fort Defiance today." He finished the contents of the can and crumpled it in his hand and handed it to me.

"But your Dad orders parts on Thursdays so you have to deliver them on Saturdays," I argued while I stooped down and placed the crumpled can in the sack of empties. I forced a cold can from the plastic mesh from the other sack and straightened myself up. When I pulled the tab, cold beer gushed over my hand. I immediately handed it to Tom.

Tom raised the can quickly to his mouth and took a long gulp. When he was through, he placed the can between his thighs and responded to my remark.

"You must understand, Dad and I have not spent time together for a while when I was in Viet Nam," he explained.

"You and your Dad, you both seem to enjoy each other's company even if you see each other every week. But your Mom, I don't think she cares to be around me week after week. She doesn't have to say it. I can feel it."

"I don't think so," he said.

"What do you know? You are not around each other."

There was silence between us for a few miles. The only sound I could hear was the gulping of beer. Then a flash of hope that I might be able to convince him to make this trip the last one for a long time came over me. I tried to retrieve the lost momentum of the conversation.

"I don't see my parents at all. Why should we see yours every weekend?" I continued. "And another thing, I thought when people get married, they try to be a little bit more independent, lead their own lives."

Tom drank the last gulp of beer and asked for another one. I handed him another cold can in exchange for his empty one. He opened it himself and took a swallow.

"Honey, you don't realize I'm doing this for your sake. I want us to go there often because I want to prove to Mom you are a worthy woman," he said softly.

"What?" I heard myself scream. My temper flared. My eyes flashed in anger. I said indignantly, "Me? Worthy of your mother?

Just who the hell does she think she is? Has it ever occurred to her that you might not be worthy of me?"

"Honey," he said.

"Don't honey me!" I continued my tirade. "You... you and your family... you all sound so superior. Has any of you accomplished anything?" I threw my face into the palm of my hands and wept.

"That's not what I meant," Tom said, apologetically.

"That's how it came out," I cried, although my anger was now dissipating. "What's your mother's standard for rating people, anyway?"

He did not answer, and the rest of the trip was spent in total silence. It was so quiet we could hear each other's heartbeat. I kept thinking, here were another two days in our lives when Clay dictated the activities for the weekend. A domineering father and husband, he decided exactly when we must cook, eat, go fishing, quit fishing, play horseshoes, quit playing horseshoes. Peggy and Tom might have adapted to this arrangement, but I was finding it encumbering my freedom. I woefully remembered Mother and Father who had tried to harness me in the past and how I had managed to do things my way, anyhow. And I had thought of my life then as constricting, suffocating. Now my ration of liberty reached the pits. I submitted to the dictates of a husband who yielded to the orders of his father.

Tom swung the car into a muddy road. The bright afternoon sun was melting the snow that had blanketed the lawn around the doublewide trailer of Clay and Peggy, turning it into reddish brown, slushy mud. From a distance, I could see Clay scrubbing his barbecue grill, getting ready for the big cookout.

Severe winters never prevented Clay from cooking outdoors. A self-styled chef, he was very meticulous about the art of charbroiling steaks. He insisted that the charcoal must be a good distance below the grill, and ash-white hot. He used only two-inch thick slabs of special cut T-bones and his own secret method of timing for perfect medium rare steaks.

We unloaded our overnight bags and went our separate ways. As usual, Tom helped his father prepare the meats for grilling. While they did this, they imbibed their favorite beverages, beer for Tom, Canadian Club and grapefruit for Clay. Meanwhile, I joined Peggy in the kitchen to bake potatoes and fix pungent sauces. Doing this job weekly, we had run out of things to talk about. We were two women as dissimilar as raw sewage and exquisite cologne. We had entirely different interests and philosophies, style and substance, goals and objectives, and shared absolutely nothing in common except the love for, and of, a common man, Tom. We had each other's company, not by our own choice, but in deference to the pleasures of our husbands. What impoverished lives plain old wives have, I thought. At least, I had a career to occupy my mind other hours of the day. When occasions arose, I expressed my opinions to Tom, something I had never seen Peggy do to Clay. Perhaps, that was what's griping her. All these weekends she probably had been dying to ask her husband to stop inviting us over. She just couldn't do it. As I chopped onions and hot chili peppers, I could feel the pressure building up between us by the minute, like a time bomb ready to explode. To the best of our abilities, however, we managed to act civil towards each other.

Like clockwork, Peggy removed from the oven the baked potatoes that had been individually wrapped in aluminum foil, and placed them on a tray, while I set the plates, spoons, and forks, and napkins on the table. Tom and Clay entered the door with the steaming hot juicy slabs of meat for distribution.

We had barely sat on our respective chairs when the phone rang. Peggy rushed to answer it. It's mother, Peggy told us, then continued their chat over the telephone. After Peggy had hung up the telephone, she returned to her seat and began to slice her steak.

"My mother has not changed one bit," she laughed, shaking her head. Then she directed her next statement to me. "Did you know that she disowned Tommy when he married his first wife? Well, you know, she's Mexican. When I told Mother Tommy's new wife is a Filipino, she came totally, utterly unglued. She said she'd see him in the life thereafter. And guess what she said when I told her you're a civil engineer?"

I was afraid to ask, but I braved it. "What?"

She answered, in a voice one octave higher than her normal one. "Big deal! My servant in the Philippines was also a civil engineer." Her eyes had a sadistic sort of gleam. Instinct told me she meant to educe some raw emotions and a fight, but I cautioned myself to consider the source and simply ignore the statement. Instead, I focused my attention on my husband to check on his reaction. There he was, busy putting a dollop of sour cream on his baked potato.

Peggy's shard-edged words might have not impaled me but it did tickle Clay's imagination. After he had hurt his back in the logging business, he had tried selling hats and gloves and insurance. But his attempts at self-employment had been mercifully short-lived. He then tried to work for the government. That was where he had been for years now—as the Roads Superintendent of the Bureau of Indian Affairs. He excelled at operating and maintaining heavy equipment but he had one problem. Like my father, he did not have a piece of paper that said he was an engineer, therefore, if he intended to retire from his job, he could only look forward to a lifetime sentence of working for engineers. And in the Navajo reservation, that meant *working for Navajo engineers.*

"Talking about engineers," he growled in between chomps of his rare steak, "they're worthless. Like my boss. The bastard doesn't even know how to operate a backhoe. You know, Tommy, them goddamn engineers have 'em degrees that don't mean nothing."

The shrapnel in Clay's words shattered my cool and raised my hackles. I had been insulted, kicked at, and spat on in engineering school for five-and-a-half miserable years. My nose had been scraped from pressure against chainlink fences. I had suffered through two board examinations. I had not done all those sacrifices only to listen to a person of the laboring class desecrate my diploma. I felt scorching heat in my ears as blood rose to my head. As reactionary as I had been to this issue, I managed to try to take Clay's statement as though he did not mean it, to give him a graceful way out.

"Watch it there," I cautioned, forcing a smile on my face. "Let's not forget daugher-in-law here is a civil engineer. Her degree might mean the whole world to her."

Clay turned to me, irritated. "Well, dammit, can you operate a backhoe?" he barked out the words. There was a heightened color on his bald head.

I was stunned. He totally ignored the diplomatic exit I had provided him. I studied his face. Realizing I had no other choice but to bark back, I erased the smile from my face, making sure not a ripple showed on my face. "No." I returned Clay's gaze as steady as his own and said distinctly and cuttingly, "I don't know how to operate a backhoe. Most engineers don't. We don't have to know how to operate a backhoe. That kind of work is for peons. That is what peons are for. There are peons and there are engineers. And there's a hell of a lot of difference between peons and engineers. Don't you forget that." I pronounced the word peon as if it was the filthiest word ever found in the dictionary. Now it was my eyes' turn to glisten with the thrill of devastating an ego.

Clay shot me a stare that could kill.

I tore my eyes away from him and concentrated on my steak. I could only blame myself for getting entangled into this in-law jam. Clay had openly discouraged me from marrying into his family when Tom and I were living together. "Find you another man," he had advised me one evening. "Marry someone of your own race. You will probably be happier." I had resented his admonition and indignantly, I remarked, "Don't concern yourself. I'll marry whomever I want to marry. Nobody but nobody, not even my own parents, can tell me whom I should marry." As the wretched weekend dragged on, I wondered, perhaps a hundred times, if there might have been some nuggets of wisdom in his advice. It crossed my mind, too, that without knowing it, weekend tortures like this might have been the reason I had promised myself when I was little never ever to get married when I grew up.

Sunday brought excitement back to my life. It was time to go home. As we were driving back to Albuquerque, I was conditioning my mind for another day yet of frustration. This time in City Hall, again, for tomorrow would be the beginning of another workweek. The visit to Peggy and Clay had just completed my life's cycle of rolling with the punches and getting up before the count of ten. It was time to get on my feet again to beat the bell and courageously face fresh blows from the other ring—City Hall.

Coffee breaks at the basement of City Hall were a traditional morning and afternoon affair of the male engineers, secretaries and draftsmen. Few events occurred in the Department of Public Works—promotions, demotions, hirings, firings, illicit affairs, and scandals—which were not discussed during coffee breaks long before official word was published on pink slips or memoranda. The coffee shop was generally a free congenial area where the engineers, draftsmen, and clerks temporarily crossed over ranks. It was not unusual, therefore, that the rumor of the new engineer being an impostor flew beyond the circle of the male engineers and reached me.

Indeed, the engineer whom everybody called Rick Elliott turned out to be a con artist. The man with rich tastes and demeanor, dapper in his expensive suits and silk ties was an impostor, an ex-convict who had romanced, in a ruse, a clerk in the office of the State Board of Registration for Professional Engineers. He stole a blank signed certificate and the name of a long dead engineer which he had calligraphed on it. Rick Elliott, whose real name was something else, had fooled Hensch and his lieutenants and skipped town before he could be arraigned.

The impostor's disappearance opened the Senior Designer slot once more. Now a registered professional engineer in the State of New Mexico, I set my sight firmly on the position. The memory of the first rejection still lingered in my mind. I remembered very clearly that Hensch had refused to give it to me because I lacked a requirement, which was the registration. There had not been any new engineers in City Hall who would be a competitive threat, so I geared up to claw my way to the promotion especially now that it was already being advertised statewide. But, like a ping-pong ball, my request to be considered for the job was bounced from one supervisor to another until it landed on Hensch's hands once more.

A wave of frustration inundated me at the thought of another confrontation with this man and his prejudices. I must brave the storm once again. My past struggles had made me poignantly aware that only the wary are given the opportunity to survive, and only those who fight succeed in the effort; that I must not give up without a shred of guts. But first, I brainwashed myself about the manner in which I would present my case. *Don't cry. Never in front of those men. Steer away from emotional nonsense or you're finished.* However, these mind conditionings were easier said than done. All my struggling life, I had never found the equivalent of the pain of standing tall, grimacing in anticipation of the flogging of rejection for being an Asian female engineer in America. When Hensch and I sat face to face across his desk, a cold silence fell in the room. My elbow anchored on the table, my palm on my face, covering my nose and mouth, I took a couple of deep breaths, my eyes staring but unseeing. When I was confident my voice was not going to quiver, I spoke calmly, without preliminary. "Why don't you want to consider me for the senior designer position?" My face was taut. My eyes penetrating.

Hensch placed his black pen back to its holder. A patronizing smile spread across his face. "Who told you so? I haven't made up my mind yet," he said.

"Well," I said, brandishing the newspaper clipping from my purse before his startled eyes. "What about this in last night's paper? This tells me you are not hiring anyone from among the City employees."

Flushed from embarrassment over the information at my fingertips, Hensch laughed nervously. He rose from his desk and walked to the window, gnashing his jaws, then he turned around.

"You won't do, Celia," he stated categorically. "You just won't do."

I asked him just what he meant. And he explained.

"You're an immigrant, he said. "You're a woman. If you're not able to design something correctly, your action would not create the right impression for the City. You see, I'm trying to save you from embarrassment."

His words, spoken through clenched jaws, had just shut the door for further discussions and demolished every room for compromises. He continued.

"Besides, I have other plans for you. I will make you the chief of the coding group when I computerize the drafting room records. That's a job more fitting for a woman."

"What!" I squirmed. Anger and self-pity swelled within me. My lower lip began to tremble, but I bit it to stop it. Each breath that I took became heavier than the first. My calm was deserting me now. I had set my emotional strength against this ruthless bigot and it began to look as if he would win and I would break down in tears. I could no longer repress the fear. I rose and rushed out to the hall and ran to the restroom. As soon as I closed the door behind me, I cried out my frustration. Only the ceramic sink and chrome water faucets witnessed my sobs. When self-indulgence flickered out, I rinsed my face, blending water with the tears in an effort to get the red out of my eyes before going back to my desk.

The nerve-wracking incident followed me home. Even at the dinner table, the endless picture of myself struggling to contain my pent-up anger and frustration and to maintain my dignity before Erwin Hensch clamped my attention. Everything seemed magnified: my sense of vulnerability in the American male engineer's world, my sense of commitment to my marriage, to a man who happened to be an American. These strong feelings rubbed against each other until they created sparks.

"Don't you think he's wrong?" I snarled at Tom.

"What are you talking about?" he asked.

"Hensch," I said. "He doesn't want to promote me. I have the degree, the experience, the registration, and he just flat out refused to consider me for the Design Engineer position. The last time the position was vacant he told me I could not have it because I was not registered in this country. Now that I'm registered he says he plans to make me head clerk. Isn't that wrong?" I was beginning to get incensed once more. I stopped eating altogether.

"It's wrong," Tom muttered more to himself than to me. He sounded unsure. He took a bite of fried pork chops.

His words grated on my nerves. With narrowed eyes, I summed his face up in disgust. "It's wrong, that's all you can say? It's wrong?" I was nearly screaming with anger.

The look of casualness peeled off his face. Having captured his full attention, I continued, my voice filled with brutal contempt. "What kind of a goddamned husband are you? You know ours is a mixed marriage. If this had happened to you in my country, I'd definitely do something to correct the wrong if I have to write the president. We are in your country; these are your people. They are trampling all over me. Can't you see? You yourself probably don't think I can do the job, do you? This is America, right? Everybody's got a chance, right? All I'm asking is a chance to be considered for the job because I am qualified. I meet the requirements of the position."

The words poured out of me so forcefully and cleanly that at the end, I felt drained. Before I knew it, hot wild tears of self-indulgence blurred my eyes. This time I let them stream freely down my cheeks.

Apologies followed the torrent of emotions. After several moments of awkward silence, we tried to banter and maintain good spirits, but sick appetites exposed the true state of affairs. Neither of us knew what the other was thinking. Until one week later.

A surprising event took place. It was stunning enough to pump new blood to my faltering efforts to extract professional recognition. It turned out that Tom, pushed by my tantrum, had contacted a state senator who started turning the tide in my favor. The senator phoned the City Manager, who in turn ordered Hensch to take a good look at my qualifications or be prepared for the consequences.

Within a few days, I walked into a spanking new, brighter world. Hensch's assistant called me in his office to inform me of a pay raise and a change of title, but same job. Hensch was still going to hire a man for the Senior Designer position. While it was just a token promotion designed to shut me up, the news gave me an instantaneous feeling of lightheartedness. As I stepped out of the door, the assistant's voice chased me.

"What does your husband do?" he asked.

I paused, mystified by the inconsequential question. I turned around and examined the man's face. He was seriously waiting for my response. It seemed of paramount importance to him.

"He's a student at the university," I replied reluctantly. Before I closed the door, I looked behind me. The assistant waved goodbye with his four fingers, a smile plastered on his face. I walked out of the door, completely baffled.

From that moment to the time that the first check with a bigger take-home pay touched my fingertips, I savored the sweet morsel of victory. But something in the manner by which I got Hensch's compromise left a bitter taste in my mouth. Why had it taken my husband's intervention to settle a simple question of equity? Had my husband, a white man, not told the State senator, a white man, who in turn told the City Manager, a white man, who ordered Hensch, another white man, to do the right thing, the wheels of the compromise process would have never even started turning. In this chain of events, one common link stood out. The participants were all white males. Clearly, in the basic arithmetic of the sphere I was in, it all added up in my mind. White men called the shots; they pushed the buttons. They had mapped out the way to the rainbow for one another; each man needed only the motivation to explore the route, and the pot of gold at its end was his for the asking. The question *"What does your husband do?"* lingered in my mind long after the token promotion, setting my thoughts in motion, curiously focusing on my husband. *What does your husband do?* His own people apparently expected him, not me, his wife, to be doing something, since he was able to force Hensch and his gang off their loop. He possessed a certain power. *What does your husband do?* A parts man in a store that sold heavy equipment, he wrote down and chased orders for parts for backhoes and compactors. He did specialized clerical work, a decent job. As an oceanography student, he studied marine life and the future of harvesting food from the ocean floor. But did these occupations enable him to wield such a powerful thrust? Definitely not. There was something in him that provided the magic and the impetus in the drama that eventually got Hensch's attention. My thoughts churned until the missing part of the equation leaped from my mind. He was a white man who possessed the inherent qualification for success in America. In one light stroke, he had set a fire for me when I had mercifully exhausted all my matchsticks and tinders. I thought, imagine the things he could be doing for himself, if I could help him ignite his inner drive. A little voice kept telling me this was the path to explore. He did something for me. I'd do something for him. We could do a lot for each other—for mutual good. I thought the baffling question *"What does your husband do"* through and through until it was no longer a puzzle. It was now just a task to be pursued.

# Chapter 16

# The Third Rung

I found a sense of excitement at the prospect of laying out the cornerstone of my new plan. My target was still the engineering arena. Through the seemingly impenetrable network of the white American men who controlled it, I could see clearly where I was going. But first, some preliminary work must be done.

The white male's natural inborn advantage in the American society as evidenced by Tom's successful intervention in my fight for professional recognition amazed me. Tom didn't know he had jolted me to attention and forced me to look, from a vantage point, at him, myself, and us. The question *"What does your husband do?"* would not leave me. At night I resisted sleep and dwelt on my feeling and conviction that there must be something I should do. Bits and pieces of his life paraded in front of my eyes and I gave them close and careful scrutiny. A college drop-out who had almost become a priest; a would-be logger who would raise and support his own family; a failed husband after eighteen months of his first marriage; a father separated from his children; a Catholic plagued by guilt; a specialized clerk making paltry income. Now he was taking a stab at a new marriage—to a fiercely determined, ambitious civil engineer. Trapped in tough cords of circumstances that did not mesh, I could see him struggling to free himself. He did not know exactly how and where to cut the unyielding fibers.

My two semesters of college psychology came flying into action. Tom's problem zoomed clearly into my view: he was tiptoeing across a tightrope balancing his guilt over a failed past marriage and children on one shoulder and his fear of an imminent failure on the other. He was hardly at peace with himself, how could he be at peace with me? The more I analyzed his problems, the more my own personal woes seemed like very small potatoes. At least my only gripe was the City

Hall men wouldn't give me the time of day. This man did not even know what his was, let alone what to do about it. I concluded that considering his intervention in my uphill battle for professional recognition, and the weight it had carried, this one well-calculated shift in gear in *my* warship would win our personal battles.

I had tried everything to make him spend more time with me at night. I had pouted, begged, cried, clammed up. I had worried about him and told him so. I didn't care any more if he came home or not and had told him so. All to no avail.

"Drinking beer with friends relaxes me," he had often reasoned. "Don't try to change me; you'll just be wasting your time and energy."

Undaunted, I had persisted, employing other methods. I had even pretended to drink alone at home to give him the impression that if I couldn't lick him, I'd join him. Still, all my efforts fell flat.

"Beer is part of my family," he had asserted during an argument. "Nothing is going to change that," he declared.

Very well, I had conceded. But my conscience reminded me frequently of the wasted minutes; important minutes he could have been using for his life, and ours.

I figured he was bored. He needed an outlet for the energy he had left after his full-time job as a partsman. He needed something to do. He needed a problem to solve. He needed a goal to reach. He needed a challenge. Since I figured this out, I also figured it was my job to provide him the missing piece of his puzzle. The missing link would cure our ailing marriage and could, quite conceivably, advance my own professional agenda. I could hardly wait to work on Tom. Many times, I stared at him, wondering if the moment was right for the inauguration of my new plan.

"What?" he would ask, mystified at my weird actions.

The time to discuss my grand scheme came one day at Shakey's Pizza Parlor. The waitress laid a tray of pizza that smelled heavily of oregano and a pitcher of cold light beer on our table. I tore away a wedge of the steaming pizza and cut the stringy cheese with my fingers. After my first bite, I embarked on my rehearsed speech for Tom.

"You know," I started. "I have always maintained that for a person to get ahead in life, he or she must have at least one of these four things: a degree or a profession, a trade or craft, a business of his own, or be born of rich parents."

Tom took a big swig of beer then transferred a wedge of pizza on a paper plate in front of him. He quietly went through his standard preliminary motions before taking a bite of any food from a plate: napkin on his thigh, and on the food, a dash of salt, several shakes of black pepper, a pinch of crushed hot chili peppers. Satisfied that he had spiced the pizza enough to his taste, he carefully lifted it and took a big bite, and focused his eyes intensely on me. His silence brought back, for a second, memories of our courtship in Manila. Inspired by the thoughtful attention reminiscent of those days, I launched my dissertation.

"Let's take your case. You tried the degree route, it did not work. You were apparently not cut for it. Your parents are not rich. Even if they were, they had already disowned you for marrying me. So that took care of that route. Which means, of the four routes, you have two left—trade and business. Count business out because we don't have the money for capital. Even if we did have the money, we don't know what kind of business you should have. That leaves trade."

Through Tom's zealous attention, I could see a rich vein of ore in him just waiting to be mined. It needed only the slightest tap. I hammered on.

"What kind of trade do you know?" I pulled another wedge of pizza and took a bite from it while waiting for his answer.

He lit a Camel. "Logging."

I laughed. "Forget logging; we live in a desert. What else by way of trade do you know?" I probed.

He talked about the things he had done in the service. He had traveled far and wide. He had been a purchasing agent. He had done and taught computer data entry to the lower sergeants.

"Those are not really trades. I am talking about occupations where hands are used like auto mechanics, equipment operators, and machinists. That kind of stuff. Do you know any of those trades or crafts?"

I sprinkled a pinch of crushed hot dried chili peppers on the pizza before I took another bite. When he did not answer, I brought out the punch line.

"Would you consider learning one?" I asked.

"Like what?" He blew a circle of smoke in the air, his eyes not leaving mine.

I smiled and wagged my finger like a salesman ready to close a sale. I fished from my purse a Technical-Vocational Institute brochure, which I had obtained earlier for this very event.

"I just happened to have this little thing."

I moved the large pizza tray to the side of the table and on its place I flattened the catalog. Together we leafed through its pages, between bites of pizza and swigs of beer, completely impervious to the frantic activities around us. We read through the listing course by course, item by item. Every now and then, I examined Tom's face, and waited for one or two of his few words.

"May I make a suggestion?" I asked when I heard nothing from him. "How about this one—Print Reading for Welders? For two bucks a course, how can you lose? If it does not work, try another subject until you find one that interests you. It beats going to the bar after five every night. What do you guys talk about in the bar night after night anyway?"

A shade of wonder came into Tom's eyes. The idea held appeal. With eight years of armed service behind him, he was at home with regimented boundaries. He acknowledged my suggestion in his normal word-scarce way: "We'll see."

When our meal ended, we walked out in silence. I was feeling a bit lighthearted. The unloading of my thoughts to Tom, his receptiveness to them, the several long swallows of beer, as I examined the causes of my giddiness, I realized how nice it was to have someone in America who cared enough to listen to me.

Action packed the weeks that followed. Tom did enroll for the course on print reading. It was a joy for me to come home from work and watch him do something productive. It was a delight just to find his face there, period. Every Monday, Wednesday, and Friday nights, he attended classes. Every Tuesday and Thursday, he studied and did his homework—at home. Between buying school supplies, studying, preparing and going to school, he found no more time to visit friends in the watering holes.

It was a smashing success just judging the opening act. I patted my back for such an insightful idea, and Tom's for accepting the challenge. A great weight had been lifted from me and the prospect of changing the complexion of the future seemed within reach. He seemed pretty challenged. From a distance, I watched him learn to use the engineer's scale, triangles, graph paper, and protractor. I observed him learn to recognize the meanings of lines—my language as an engineer—on blueprints. At the end of the trimester, he completed the Print Reading Course for Beginning Welders. He received his certificate, then along with his classmates and instructor, celebrated this milestone—over a case of beer in their favorite cocktail lounge.

From that day forward, Tom discovered an interest he had not known before. Instead of proceeding to the intermediate courses on welding, he set his sights on construction. An honestly sincere man gifted with a warm personality and excellent salesmanship, he talked to men who bought parts for their construction equipment. He read construction plans with them. Here and there in his conversation, he inserted bits of information about his wife, a civil engineer who worked for the City's Department of Public Works. These men who did business with the City either by supplying construction services or construction equipment, saw how they could use Tom and me to their advantage. Every man pushed his own agenda. One handshake led to another, into the cloakrooms of power and before I knew it, opportunities piled on our doorstep. By now, we were talking the same language. We were talking construction plans. One evening he mentioned in passing about an offer from one Pete Cote. Pete Cote was a tall man with a high crooked nose and narrow drooping shoulders, a transplant from New Hampshire who had been building roads in the northern part of New Mexico for three years. Pete had asked Tom to quit his job and help Pete with his road construction business with a view toward buying into it.

"Take his offer," I goaded. "If things don't work out, you can always go back to working as a partsman. We have my salary to count on."

Encouraged, Tom quit his job and worked at Pete's business. In the beginning, he drove the 120-mile round-trip commute between Albuquerque and Santa Fe, buying and delivering materials to the sites. Later, he rode around with the superintendent who dropped him off periodically to job sites. In spite of working long hours and driving all over the state, Tom scraped only enough money to make his child support payments. The exhaustion, compounded by meager paychecks brought him only frustrations. He was getting discouraged.

I knew I was mostly to blame but I could not let him get discouraged. The idea that he now moved within my province meant he was within arm's length from the field engineering job I had been coveting. Something ought to be done quickly.

In one of our Friday pizza evenings, I brought construction back into focus.

"How's Pete treating you these days?" I cast the line, for a discussion about his work and himself.

"He has been making overtures about me lending him money," he laughed, dryly, shaking his head. "I have watched him operate around other people. He's a user. I think that's what he really had in mind when he offered me to work with him."

It was the longest speech I had ever heard from him and the first time he had allowed me in his thoughts.

"Where on earth did he think you can get some money?" I asked, incredulously.

"He wants me to borrow money from some of my wealthy friends," he explained. "He knows I know the president of a savings and loan association."

"How about that!" I thought out loud, and continued: "Did he say he'll let you go if you didn't lend him some money?"

"No."

"Then you're still okay," I wheedled at him. "As long as you make enough to meet your child support obligations, don't worry about us. We'll make do with my salary until you get your feet solidly on the ground. For now, just keep learning the trade and the business, as long as he keeps you."

The grim situation continued for six months, but Tom hung on courageously. Watching projects in progress, he tried to learn every aspect of construction. He watched pipe layers install waterlines and sewers. He saw operators plow their backhoes and graders into dirt roads and create big holes and small hills, He correlated what he saw on the ground to the lines on the blueprint.

It was amazing how doors opened automatically for a white male in America. You would think Tom had received a master's degree in construction management, the way people respected his knowledge of blueprint reading. As he wove friendship within the network of white men who seemed to be bound by an unwritten code of mutual support, he continued to meet helpful people, until one day, he stumbled upon a businessman who offered to finance Tom's own construction business. In addition, the man introduced Tom to an established contractor who would be his reservoir for his initial work. Whereupon, he, my husband, became a company president overnight and I, the First Lady of the venture! That long-lost feeling of wanting to jump like a pogo stick and do a somersault shamelessly was revived in me once again.

The arrangement clicked and business boomed. For the first time in our union, Tom brought home paychecks fatter than mine. My heart no longer pounded at the thought of a bouncing check whenever we paid for our Friday pizza and beer splurges, Our savings book darkened with the ink of entries under the deposits column. Dinners of prime rib and lobster became possible even without long-range planning. I filled Mother's mail orders for more money. Without any sentiments, we saw the old Dodge Dart off and drove around like crazy in a new gas-guzzling luxury car.

Tom reveled on his newly discovered capabilities and greatly improved earning capacity. His mind buzzed with ideas of expanding both, leaving no room for petty thoughts about me and the men around my profession. Just like I had envisioned him to be, he became a new person—strong and resilient, confident of his own strength. With his busy schedule, his insane jealousies and preoccupation with my every movement went with the wind.

My existence, however, as an engineer non-entity persisted. Whenever we attended the engineers' functions, people now assumed Tom was the engineer. When either of us apologetically corrected them, the conversations usually halted to a deathly silence. By clamming up, the men managed to shoo the issue away. In City Hall, the male engineers still reigned supreme. Although politics had forced Hensch to give me raises in pay, he never gave me the progressively responsible experience that accompanied the money. My mind, now clear of problems of the marital kind, focused on this situation. It churned out until one thought stood out. I needed to seek someplace the responsibility and prestige I was being deprived of. But I cautioned myself against quitting my job. Resignation would only be tantamount to running away from the problem, thus delivering on the hands of the male engineers, especially Hensch, their satisfaction. I was not possessed of such generosity. I had every intention to claw them by the collar and force them to see my contentions squarely. Then, and only then would I leave on my own terms, when I was good and ready. Since they had already locked up all doors on my face, the key to other opportunities of engineering responsibility and prestige lay on my hands alone. On and on, my mind went as though committed to a treadmill. Then it dawned on me: my engineering registration. Here was the privilege I happened to have—the license to practice as a professional engineer. I could do private practice without leaving City Hall. I'd moonlight.

I tossed in my mind the idea of moonlighting for a while. I kept thinking if the men in City Hall did not want, or were afraid, to give me heavier responsibilities, who would do it outside City Hall? Some businesses prohibit their employees from moonlighting; some people figure that what you do in your own time is your own business. I was a member of the latter group and I believe that as long as I create no conflict of interest in my employment, a little freelancing on the side is okay. In fact, it is beyond okay. At that time, I felt the change in pace both in terms of type of work, objectives, and deadlines would keep me fresh and make me a better engineer. I'd also pick up skills needed in case I decided to do freelance work full time. Such skills like the art of negotiation, hustling work, and writing off lunch. Finding clients is possible, I assured myself when I began to entertain doubts. Armed with renewed optimism, I announced my intention to do engineering work on the side, above board and legitimate, first to Tom then to the men above me in City Hall.

Then it hit me. It would not be that easy. So far, nothing had ever been a cakewalk. I would have to get Erwin Hensch's approval if I were to operate my private consulting legitimately. This man, surely, would erect a barricade for me again, as he had tried predictably and vigorously in the past. But I had news for him. I had learned, in addition to patience, to be one step ahead of the men in general, because I had been prone to encountering too many barriers in the past, and had found that one single pace ahead always made all the difference in the race for survival. On top of that, sleuthing talents of Agatha Christie were needed. I formulated a methodical strategy to counter his disapproval of my moonlighting permit. I meticulously researched the other engineers, to find out who had been moonlighting, for how long, what kind of moonlighting they did, and who approved their permits. Very carefully, I sorted out all the discoveries out to catch the single thread that would unravel the snarl of Erwin Hensch's forthcoming yarn of lies. When time came for him to act on my request for a permit, he summoned me to his office.

My heart pounded again in anticipation of another stormy encounter with the man and his biases. I took a deep breath before tapping his door.

"What is this request to moonlight?" he said after he motioned me to sit down. His face exhibited his usual signs of adamance: knitted brows, lips curved downward, a swollen vein dividing his forehead. "I will disapprove it."

"May I know why?" I asked, my eyes fixed on his.

"Well, this moonlighting business is more serious than you think. You could embarrass the City as well as yourself."

I was irritated. "But why do you keep telling me I'd embarrass everybody with my engineering? I've been here three years now. Have I embarrassed you? Didn't everything that I designed get built? What seems to be the problem?" I asked in quick succession.

Hensch wagged his finger at me. "Hey, listen to me," he said. "Something could go wrong, you could get sued, your social life could be ruined, you could..."

"Will you stop concerning yourself," I interrupted impatiently. "Those are my problems, not yours."

"Oh yes, they're mine too. If I gave you the permit and you did something wrong, I could be blamed. I have a high-profile job. The press is always after me. You might have to testify as an expert witness," he said.

"So, what's the big deal? I can be an expert witness, too."

"You have no idea know what you're getting into."

"Mr. Hensch, please, let's not forget I am as engineer as you are."

The connotation of equality in my words shot through Hensch. Anger pushed him up from his chair and he began to walk around in the room. His face reddened, the vein on his forehead seemed to throb and turn purplish. He returned to his chair.

"Let's put it this way, young lady, I don't allow my engineers to moonlight and I'm not about to start now," he stated with the sound of finality. "That's the way it's going to be and that's the end of our discussion."

"Not quite yet, please," I protested, firmly. There was steel in my voice. "I'd like to know first when you put an end to this moonlighting business. Tell me," I asked, looking at him squarely.

"It's been two or three years now, I don't remember."

"Will you allow me to show you something?" I asked without any intention of waiting for his permission. Once more the value of complete preparation was about to be demonstrated. I dug into my purse for the information I had researched. I flattened the documents in front of his face. "Will you kindly tell me then why engineer George Paul's moonlighting permit is current? How about surveyor LaMonte Urban's? It is also current. I understand you and he belong to the same church." I paused to let my point sink home. "What gives around here, anyway?"

Hensch flushed. He was accustomed to issue commands, not answer questions. The vein on his forehead bulged. His eyes widened, his composure rattled by the amount of information heaped on him. At this moment around him was an aura of defeat. The façade that he thought opaque—therefore he did not need to cover—was on the verge of transparency. He was a pathetic stricken figure who laid in pieces at my feet.

"All right, all right," he returned with vigor. He reached for a ball pen inside his desk drawer. He wagged the pen at me. "I'll sign your permit on condition you will not do any work within the city limits and up to five miles outside its perimeter. I don't want any conflict-of-interest and unfair-competition complaints from private consultants."

"That's fine," I said, struggling to smile with dignity. I did not want to appear too jubilant. "As long as you gave the same restrictions to the moonlighting men."

He gave me one last baleful look before affixing his signature of approval on the permit.

"Thank you," I said, smugly, and I cast him a glance of triumph on my way out of his office.

While the "gotcha" approach worked for me, the contempt in his eyes warned me that it would not produce a smooth, ongoing relationship; that until he dropped out, I had not really won.

# Chapter 17

✦

# The Manhole, at Last

*"There is hardly anything in the world that some man cannot make a little worse and sell a little cheaper and the people who consider price only are this man's lawful prey."*

— **John Ruskin**

The sign on the wall of a Baskin Robbins ice cream parlor got my attention. True, I thought to myself, but the thing does not have to be a little worse. Through some ingenuity, it can be made a little more economical but a trifle more attractive. I wasn't thinking dessert. I was considering moonlighting as an engineer. The market I'd penetrate in the business zoomed into view: land developers who wouldn't care if a man or a woman, an Asian or an African did the engineering of their project as long as they shelled out slightly less money for it. Everybody has a price; each soul a tag. I'd find these people, and with a little promotion, they'd find me. They'd probably be more interested in finding me than the other way around. I was smiling inside with a purring satisfaction with my game plan. I'd pass the word to the surveyor who had entrusted me with my very first job in the United States. He would pass it on to clients who would ask for the name of an engineer with a reasonable price.

Within days of getting my private consulting permit, I was working on my first project—the design of the extension of a 300-foot long sanitary sewer for a commercial development 25 miles outside Albuquerque. I worked on it with burning fervor. On red alert after Hensch's "gotcha" retreat, I ensured that no City time, materials, or furnishings were used on my project. For two nights after supper, I piled the dirty dishes in the sink and used the table as my drawing board and designed the sewer system. I paid a moonlighting draftsman to draw up the plan in his house, and a moonlighting woman to type the specifications and estimate on her typewriter in her house. My client paid me $500 for the finished product. The elation that I felt when I deposited the check can never be surpassed. I felt so wealthy, as if I could reduce the national deficit. It was like Independence Day! I wasn't a would-be consultant anymore. I had made my plunge. My first consulting project was safely tucked under my belt. Even though it was small, I was its star, the principal responsible party. I wrote to my father and bragged. He wrote back and told me he had rushed to Bulacan to brag about his daughter, *the successful consulting engineer.*

After a month, the sanitary sewer was built. Buried seven feet below the ground, the first monument to my gutsy, independent show of professional prowess in the United States was invisible to the ordinary layman, but word about my work and price spread like hot gossip outside Albuquerque. The floodgates opened. My first client, satisfied with what he had gotten, came back and gave me more business. His friends contacted me to design housing subdivisions. Friends and relatives of friends came my way, hiring me to engineer mobile home parks, big and small. When a dam in Idaho collapsed and hit national headlines, I received an offer to check a small dam that crossed a private mountain property. The owner of a construction firm that laid pipes for gas companies in New Mexico and Texas asked me to design the relocation of a pipeline across a dry river bed. There were interesting offers and projects. A state senator invited me to masterplan a sprawling acreage located one hundred fifty miles west of Albuquerque. The awesome size of the proposed development almost tempted me to accept the invitation, but for some reason known only to my instincts, I turned him down. Two months later, the senator's name hit the front pages of the newspapers regularly. He was indicted, and eventually served time, for operating a prostitution farm on that very piece of property. A wealthy developer paid me to design a mobile home park on a large tract of land that had been used as sewage sludge drying bed. I could still taste the penetrating smell of the sediment that had resulted from the processing of human wastes.

Word got around. Serious land developers and professional respect came my way. Clients did not think I ran a powder-puff operation. It reached profitable peaks.

Meanwhile, Tom continued establishing himself as a shrewd entrepreneur, wheeling and dealing like neither of us imagined he could. He built a strong network of support with bankers and other businessmen. He diversified into real estate and other investments. On speculation, he bought out-of-the-way items that he thought he could sell for profit later. One day, he came home with a seven-foot-long elephant tusk complete with legal papers. A friend had to help him carry and maneuver the hundred-pound ivory around the house.

Soon, I had squirreled away enough money from my moonlighting and Tom's income and investments. Our lifestyle changed dramatically. Dinners of prime rib and lobster now included two or more guests. Communications between my family and me necessitated periodic field trips to the Philippines to update Father about engineering consulting in America. Vacations meant distant exotic places like Hawaii and Hong Kong.

In early 1973, the Supreme Court launched an emotional debate over abortion. The nation's highest court ruled that "personal privacy rights are broad enough to encompass a woman's decision whether or not to terminate her pregnancy." The Roe vs. Wade decision invalidated abortion statutes in 46 states. A week later in another front, the United States and Viet Nam signed the agreement to end the war and restore peace in the embattled southeast Asian country.

While Americans were embroiled in issues concerning overseas peace and the woman's anatomy, something was secretly beleaguering me. My biological clock was ticking frantically. Reminders about my body kept popping. A lot more pregnant women seemed to walk the streets. Announcements about new babies dominated the news from friends in the Philippines. I was, with alarming intensity, being drawn to magazine articles on motherhood. I was now thirty-one years old. My reproduction years would soon be history.

On one of our visits to Fort Defiance, I overheard a conversation about a new kitten that my mother-in-law brought home for a pet.

"Let her have a set of litter before getting her spayed," Clay suggested. "Cats become better cats after they've had kittens."

Clay's statement clung to my mind like glue for days. I kept thinking, could that be true about female humans? Could I be a better person after I've had a child? It was a monumental case to debate. I told Tom the cat story and he collapsed in laughter. Perhaps, the urgency of the issue of my diminishing childbearing years had made me too sensitive, because for the first time I did not find his chortle contagious. Instead, I tried to interpret it. I wondered if the laughter was his way of saying "No, dear, you're hopeless. Nothing can improve you." Or was it "Better woman after childbirth? You're already perfect. What are you talking about?" Then it hit me. My parenthood ought to concern him also. I forced the issue on him. We discussed it thoroughly, leaving no facets unturned. We had to make a critical decision in our marriage. We had to choose: either we have a baby very quickly or forget about raising a family altogether. Now or never. We decided to start a family.

A couple of months later, our little adobe house suddenly seemed too cramped, too musty. In the shower stall, the curtains looked too mildewy, the floor too rough. With the seed of a baby planted in my belly, it did not take much to convince ourselves about moving to spacier, fresher quarters. We decided to build a decent house near the foothills.

Hand in hand, we watched the progress of the construction of our house, enjoying the clanging of hammer against nail and the rasp of saw against wood. Tom, gifted with fine taste, concerned himself with its interior. I concentrated on the engineering aspect, making sure the house floor would be safe from flooding problems from the abutting streets. I verified that the waterline was of the proper size and the sanitary sewer drained properly. Together, Tom and I leafed through catalogs and selected color and design of tiles, carpets, and wood cabinets.

Finally, a laborer picked up the last construction debris, the landscape man laid down the final square patch of green grass, and the vacuum cleaner whined down. We walked across the street to get a full view of our new nest. Tom straddled an arm across my shoulders and I placed my hand around his waist. As we gazed with feverish delight at our new three-level structure, we admired its majestic stance against the Sandia Mountain. We agreed it was the most gorgeous house on the block. With that, we moved in. The smell of fresh paint and varnish continued to remind us of the newness of our haven, and we savored every nook and corner of the unquestionable, visible, and tangible proof of our solidarity.

During the latter months of my pregnancy, I took an extended maternity leave with the serious intent to attend to full-time mothering and homemaking. But fifteen years of hammering away could not be silenced in three months' time. While waiting for the baby's arrival, I accepted another consulting job to keep me busy. On the eve of the baby's birth, I was at the Albuquerque Metropolitan Area Flood Control Authority, pressuring the executive engineer to expedite the review of my drainage report.

"I've got to collect from my client before I enter the hospital tonight," I stated unequivocally.

The silver-haired man shook his head, smiled and focused his eyes on my protruding belly.

"Is that baby going to be a boy?" he asked.

The following day, my destiny with obstetrics came. When for the first time the nurse presented to me a little wiggling bundle, a rush of maternal tenderness propelled me to hug my son fiercely. He looked so fragile I feared I broke his little bones. I kept admiring his dark eyes and soft, fine brown hair. When he let out a shrill cry, I was surprised to find my hand reaching for a filled aching breast to give to his tiny eager lips. It came home to me as a shock how much this tiny creature depended on me. The hand of responsibility pressed heavily on my back. The prospect scared me. My throat tightened and I heard myself bawling.

My mind zeroed in on Mother. She was also a fulfilled woman. She had brought me into this world just as I had delivered my son— writhing in piercing interminable pain only a woman who had gone through natural childbirth would ever know. Despite our differences widened by a generation gap, she had been very good to her children. No amount of money could ever repay her and Father's love and sacrifices. The least I could do would be to give them the opportunity to see the wonderland of their imaginations; the country to which they had, without a shadow of misgivings, unquestioningly entrusted their daughter's fate. Let them judge for themselves if their decisions as parents had been right. I wiped my wet cheeks and found myself slightly embarrassed at the wave of sentimentality that had engulfed me. This was so unlike me. I usually cried only to let the steam out of frustration. Indeed, childbirth is a most humbling experience.

Within three years Mother and Father flew to Albuquerque under the sponsorship of me, their naturalized American offspring. They arrived tired but enthusiastic, clutching bags of native basket materials filled with clothes and Filipino canned food: sweet jackfruit in syrup, milkfish in black bean sauce, roast pork in liver gravy, coconut milk. Tom fixed my parents a self-contained room with all the trappings of modern civilization in America: radio, tape recorder, television and stereo sets, a king-size bed with brass headboards and quilted spreads, a shining bureau. After my parents' dizziness from the long flight trailed off, they sat quietly on the edge of their comfortable bed, happily mesmerized.

&infin;&infin;&infin;

Rubbing myself dry with a towel, I looked at the mirror and thought, I'm thirty five now; I've lost my youth. I leaned closer to the mirror. My face stared back critically. It was not the same face that I had seen ten years ago. Time had somewhat dulled the clarity and sheen of the skin and the eyes. I searched for wrinkles under my eyes, then around their outer corners. There were none. I ran my fingers through my hair to hunt for grays. None surfaced. Nodding to my reflection, I felt somehow relieved. Lately, the doormen at lounges had stopped asking me for proof of age. It was because, I confirmed now, they had come to know me, and not because of wrinkles and gray hairs. It comforted me to agree that Orientals age more slowly, their skin remain taut and firm through middle age. Then alas, around seventy-five or eighty, they turn into prunes overnight. But old age is old age in any country. That will be a long time yet; don't worry about it, I consoled myself. Quite a few years will have to pass yet.

But no matter what figuring I did in my mental abacus, somehow there was this sense of loss, a feeling that time and opportunity had passed me by. I was now at the cul-de-sac of my career. End of the line. Nowhere to go, no future. Then it dawned on me: field work! My life had taken a long zigzagging detour and I had lost sight of my goal of becoming a field engineer. I must find the closure that would connect me to the fruition of the dream. Time was running out. I must get out and work as a field engineer while I still looked young. Age would soon be another hurdle. It was time to quit pressing my nose to the window. I wanted in. I must become a field engineer— soon and by all means.

The computer in my mind whirred, searching for a program for possible closure routes. Tom could help me now directly. His construction business was in fine shape. He had recently successfully bid a three-million-dollar road job. Its plans called for the construction of a main highway traversing an Indian reservation in the northern part of the state. Culverts, sanitary sewers, a water system, concrete and asphalt pavement would be involved. He could make me the field engineer of that project. He would if I asked him. He'd better.

Another alternative popped up: the City. I had been with the City faithfully for nine years now. My male counterparts had come and gone because ours was a thankless job of dealing with the public amidst pressure and bureaucracy. A city engineer needs to humor the public and possess patience to ride the bureaucratic tide. He must roll with the punches, fight brush fires. My own responsibilities as design engineer had already increased. Clearly, the City and I were designed for each other. And now, the City needed me more than I needed it. I did not have to work any more. I could negotiate with the City for a field job. Hensch, I felt sure, would assign me to the field if I asked him. By now he had learned to respect my wishes when I wanted something. He had discovered rudely on more occasions that when I wanted something, I meant business. I'd pursue it with hard-driving tenacity and I'd get it one way or another. Knowing that, he'd listen. I knew he would. He'd better.

As though committed to a churn, my mind labored on and on, around and around, designing, plotting, counter-plotting. It was powered by a steel resolve to produce a cream of a scheme, something very smooth that would only flow advantageously one way—my way.

Finally, my meticulously planned scheme was drafted. I would ask the City for a year's leave of absence to further my studies. If the men turned me down, I'd suggest a field assignment within the city. If they turned me down for that, I'd suggest a private contractor, who in my mind would be Tom. If worse came to worst, I'd quit the City and work with him as a field engineer and inspector. My mind buzzed with this wonderful plan and finally, my face broke into a satisfied smile. I was sure, beyond a shadow of doubt, the plan would go every which way but fail. The die was cast; I was going to become a field engineer one way or another.

I set out to pursue the game plan. Tom did not offer any resistance. Like a helium-filled balloon, he wafted calmly along the breeze of words I had blown towards his direction. He was willing to take me on board if all else failed with the City. With that, I turned to phase two of my scheme. Starting from the low man on the chain of command in the Department of Public Works, I tried to convince the supervisors, setting a deadline by which each one must give me his decision.

"You have your schedule, I have mine," I told every man who had anything to do with the drawn-out decision-making process within the bureaucracy.

Indeed, life had a way of dealing the deck from the bottom. Ah, the joy of telling the men and giving them deadlines. Each time I walked out of a supervisor's office, I was flooded with an overwhelming sense of power I had never felt before.

The City gave in to my demand. Hensch allowed me to become the resident engineer and inspector of a $250,000 community development project. It was going to be interesting. For the first time in local history, a woman would be the inspector and the field engineer. It would be first for the City, first for the contractor, first for the consultant, and first for me.

The project, aptly called Martineztown Rehabilitation Project, consisted of the rehabilitation of two streets in Martineztown, a depressed area in the valley. The contractor would tear out the old cracked asphalt street, remove the rusty waterline and lateral connections and replace them with new pipes and tubings. He would also remove and replace the sanitary sewer system. Upon completion of all the underground utility work, he would construct a new wider asphalt street, complete with concrete curb and gutter and sidewalk to make walking safer for the residents of the neighborhood. Hopefully, the contractor would build the street to drain properly and without birdbaths or small pools of water after a rain or after snow melted.

Hensch had chosen Martineztown Rehabilitation for me because it covered just about every aspect of the construction of a civil engineering design project. There would be concrete, asphalt, asbestos cement pipes, clay pipes, water meters, low retaining walls, drainage inlets, manholes, pressure testing. Name it, it's there. Besides, always on the watch for opportunities to put me in my rightful place, he had explained: "The other projects are dogs. They are too big for you. And Martineztown residents are Spanish people. You can relate to them. They are funny people." With the word funny, he gestured with his hand, a waving motion, clarifying it had nothing to do with hilarity but with something else.

As resident engineer and inspector, my responsibility was to see that the contractor did all his work in accordance with the approved plans and specifications. I must protect the interest of the City that would own and maintain the streets forever after the contractor's three-year warranty expired. Meanwhile, during the construction, I must also perform some public relations acts. I must appease irate residents who might be displeased by any part of the work. I must inform them ahead of time of waterline shutoffs so they could take the necessary steps to go on with their lives with as little disruption as possible.

Mother sewed several jumpsuits in reds and blues and yellows using one McCall's pattern. I wore one on my first day on the field and I walked up and down the job site, followed by a sea of eyes of the residents who had curiously come out of their houses to see what was going to happen in their neighborhood. Generations of Hispanic families had lived and died and reincarnated in this part of town. The current residents, like their ancestors, had the tendency to be jarred by any form of change that could disturb their simple, quiet existence. Some elderly men, whose sun-baked faces were deeply lined with wrinkles, asked me questions, which I tried to answer as diplomatically as possible. Upon discovery that the construction would enhance their neighborhood, and thus improve the quality of their remaining lives, the residents quietly returned to their little houses some of which were older than them. The younger, able-bodied men hung around, mystifying me. I wondered why they were neither in their own workplaces nor in schools. Moving on, I watched in fascination as the contractor's laborers performed their jobs. A heavy equipment operator uprooted big trees in seconds. With one pass, a blademan scraped the street surface, lifting big slabs of asphalt pavement and piling them on a truck. When the truck overflowed with dirt load, the driver hauled it away. Laborers in grimy grease-stained clothes demolished rusty barbed wire and chicken coop fencing. The superintendent, a tanned, erect, muscular man with wavy brown hair combed towards his back, watched the peons critically. When he noticed me standing by, he swept a glanced at me, looked at his men, then at me again with a reluctant smile. We struck a conversation. A truck loaded with broken concrete and asphalt pavement pieces stopped in front of us.

"How long have you been in the business, gal?" A deep voice came from the truck.

I craned my neck to look up at the high truck. He was a man in his early twenties, with sandy hair under a dirty backward baseball cap, blue eyes, and a bright smile.

"Twenty years," I answered jovially. A stretch, it included my five-and-a-half years in engineering school and the six months that Father had pondered the thought of drafting me in it.

The young man frowned deeply. He lifted his cap with one hand and with the fingers of the other, combed his hair back under it, and sped away without comment. The truck kicked up a cloud of dust on its path.

Later in the duration of the project, the congenial introduction turned to serious business. The superintendent fidgeted uncomfortably when I observed the construction progress. He avoided my eyes. He walked from where I was to the other end of the street. However, with determination coupled with patience, both borne of years of practice, the relationship became more cordial towards the end of the project.

A newspaper reporter got wind of the historic assignment and made an appointment with me to record the moment—in pictures— to which I delightfully agreed. I suggested that we waited until I lamped a newly built manhole because I wanted to make the pictures as symbolic as symbolic could be.

April 21, 1977. It was one of those days that a happy person would call perfect: clear blue skies, bursting sunlight, birds flirting with each other in and out of Navajo willows, glorious spring breeze. I was clad in a jumpsuit made from chocolate brown cotton fabric printed with tiny red flowers. The feminine outfit, sewn by Mother for the special occasion, had a two-inch strap crossed over each shoulder and formed an x on my back. A blue hard hat blotched with a riot of colorful stickers placed securely on my head completed the wardrobe. Holding a big flashlight in my right hand, I stood erect, all set, just waiting for the cue for the command performance.

From the street corner a few yards away, the newspaper photographer, a slight dark man with black curly hair, appeared. A brown leather camera case hung from one shoulder. When he saw me up close, a shade of confusion came into his eyes.

"Why are you wearing that?" he asked, staring at my coveralls.

I followed his gaze to a point where each strap connected to the front of my outfit with a button the size of a quarter coin.

"What's wrong with it?" I asked, perplexed.

"Engineers don't wear that," he said.

"They do now," I returned, laughing. "I want to make sure I look like a woman so that the image of a woman, not one looking like a man or a little boy, appears on the picture. I want people to be able to tell at a glance, without reading the caption; it's a woman under the hard hat. There's the reason."

He shook his head, then conceded.

"Let's go for it," he said.

He raised the flap of the brown leather case and pulled out the camera and a long cylindrical black lens. He screwed it to the face of the camera. The camera clicked as he took pictures of me from all angles in and out of a manhole. He took a shot of me squatting at the bottom of the manhole. He asked me to focus the lamp on the pipe opening inside the manhole.

"Look up," he said. "Smile."

I obliged. When I looked up, I saw another photographer, a frail girl in a plaid skirt and a sweater.

"Smile for me," she said, smiling herself.

Around and around they went, shooting while I posed emerging from the manhole, sitting on the heavy manhole cover, walking towards the manhole, on my hands and knees at the edge of the manhole. I smiled and smiled and smiled, completely oblivious of the painful lifetime journey that had brought me there.

The sun was heading west when the press people drove off to wherever their jobs propelled them, abandoning me in loneliness, mulling over my job as a field engineer. The novelty of the job had somewhat dulled in the past six hours. My excitement had already begun to fade away, leaving within me a sense of hollowness. I had this awful feeling of expecting something to happen knowing it would never come. I kept asking myself "Is that all there is?" What an absolutely crashing letdown. The field engineer was just doing another job, the continuation of the work done by the office engineer. While the field engineer enjoyed the breeze and sunlight and freedom of the outdoors, the office engineer had the warmth of controlled heating or the coolness of air-conditioning of the indoors. While the engineer confined to four walls worked with lines and letters on paper drawings, his counterpart in the open air dealt with the real things, pipes, dirt, construction materials and the people whose hands touched them.

A flood of angry questions poured out of my mind. What was

the big deal all these years that only men had been given the privilege to work as field engineers? What took so long for me to be allowed to become one? All these years, where was the blindfolded lady holding a set of balanced scales? The more I pondered the answers, the thicker my blood curdled at the thought of how the serrated-edged instruments called "discrimination" had cut a chasm through my life. It had suspended my career for more than ten years. I had been robbed of many years that could have been used to enhance it. I could have devoted that time to the science of engineering and perhaps made a lasting contribution to it. But no. All that time, the men had me reeling around and around a circle, coming and going on different tangents. It had been unfair. Very unfair. But, consider the spoils. I had become the first female field engineer in the State. I had cracked the dam of prejudices. I had made the breakthrough. The coolness of such an accomplishment was enough to dampen the heat of anger growing in my heart and to crack my face into a pleased smile. I went home after my first eight hours as a field engineer in very fine spirits, slithering with alacrity, reveling in the realization of my dream. I had touched the stars.

The picture of me smiling, looking up from the bottom of the manhole lamping it, filled half the front page of *The Albuquerque Tribune* the following day. Captioned LADY IN A MANHOLE, it recognized me as the first woman civil engineer to do field inspection full-time for the city. It also said that I had become an American citizen two years ago.

It was a day of triumph for me and for all the persons I had sought to reach—all those who have to overcome adversities of any kind!

Father wallowed in his crowning glory. He walked half a mile to a newspaper dispenser outside a Walgreen's Payless store. He borrowed a shopping cart and filled it with all the copies of the day's issue. He rolled the clumsy cart on the concrete sidewalk, back to our house, whistling, making the task seem effortless. He spent a whole week mailing them to relatives and friends in the Philippines, in Canada, and the United States. It was a week of bragging about his daughter, *the first woman field engineer in New Mexico!*

# Chapter 18

# The American Dream

The women's liberation movement that began with the burning of bras in the early '70s had matriculated to consciousness-raising events as the '80s approached. Suddenly, I found myself in the middle of workshops, leading discussions of the buzzword topics of the day such as "Superwoman Syndrome," "Dealing with Stereotyping," and "1,001 Hats." The few "made" women spoke about "Coping with Success," "Becoming Your Own Press Agent," and "Balancing Family and Career." Being the trainer, and not one of the trainees, somehow gave me a sense of achievement, but my career struggles were far from over. My employer had not yet recognized me as an engineering entity. Over the years, promotions came and went and the great white fathers continuously and consistently denied me my rightful share. Young male engineers whom I trained had sprinted to bigger, better-paying, and more prestigious positions, leaving me to eat dust at the same lowly spot at the bottom of the totem pole. The white male supervisors refused to promote me as many times as I bid. One time the City commissioned the local chapter of the National Organization for Women to investigate my complaint of discrimination. After six months of gathering information, the women declared that there had been no discrimination because my salary was as high as those of the male engineers were. The good ladies missed my point. I stressed that money was not everything. I wanted progressively responsible experience. Clearly, the feminist movement had nary a ripple effect on my own plight. In frustration, I went to a lawyer and inquired if I could file a class-action suit. He asked what class I was representing. I said all the female civil engineers. He asked, "How many are you?" I said only one, me. He told me I was not a class. The future of my career obviously rested in my own hands.

## Celia Ruiz-Tomlinson

Friends and associates asked, "Why don't you quit and find a more promising job someplace else?" I never considered that an option. If the proliferation of women's awareness workshops was any sign of the times, females in the workplace had quite a distance yet to go to find equality. A bull of a problem existed, more so in my case, and I needed to grab it by the horns. To quit meant to run away from the problem. If I turned my back to it, I'd be eyeball to eyeball with it again sooner or later.

In 1981, I accepted a temporary assignment in the Solid Waste Department, a job that all the male engineers had refused for having no expertise in sanitary landfills. I had worked with the department on various short-term assignments before, but I took the position only to create a breathing room between me and the men who for 13 years had been denying me promotion. To my surprise, the engineers resented my move! "How dare her insinuate she knows more than we do!" seemed to be the battle cry. A new conflict followed, threatening my engineering existence once more. This time the supervisors resorted to harassment tactics. First, they told me to submit a weekly report of my activities in the other department. I did. After three weeks, they changed the report requirement. They wanted me to report what I did the week before and what I planned to do the coming week. I was Ms. Agreeable; I obeyed. Then they said I needed to add a daily report. I complied. Soon reports overflowed the filing cabinet. I endured the harassment and remained Ms. Deferential, but when they gave me an unreasonably low performance evaluation mark, I just had to strike back. I demanded an explanation or a correction if the low grade had been a mistake, but they ignored me. With no other alternatives, I filed a lawsuit for on-the-job, not sexual, harassment. During the discovery phase of the litigation, lawyers saw clearly that the supervisors had singled me out for the burden of report writing. None of the male engineers could produce one iota of a report for any of their assignments. Before the march on the steps of the courthouse became imminent, the City offered, and I accepted, after playing hardball, a financial settlement. Such was my idea of exiting on my own terms and with a bang.

Realizing I had already touched my goal, I woke up one morning savoring life's richness not in a material sense, but in available options. I leaped out of bed, buoyed by the pleasure in knowing that I could do whatever I chose to do. I asked myself questions in bewilderment. Why am I getting up at six in the morning and rushing to a cold gray building that will confine me for ten hours, five days a week? Why not use the option to move out to the world, smell the flowers, or do something more challenging, more rewarding, even though it means taking a fresh risk? My nerves tingled with the sensation of wanting to go on an adventure. In a moment, it was history. I decided to take the plunge, to bolt out of the secure, snug world of employment. It was time to say goodbye to the machine that obediently churned out identical paychecks every two weeks. I was anxious to grasp a breath of cool air in a place out there that people described as rugged and cold—the world of entrepreneurship.

I supposed I had expected a festive going-away party from City Hall after I announced my resignation. After all, my departure would mark the end of an era, the passage of the tenure of the city's first female engineer. I was quite sure my adversaries would be delighted to throw a good-riddance party. But the planners of social gatherings viewed history differently, giving it less thought than I had imagined. In the end, a dozen employees including two senior draftsmen and two of my best engineer friends took me out to lunch where a surprise male stripper awaited me. As I watched the male stripper gyrate his g-stringed glistening dark muscled body, I couldn't help but smile at the irony. While a female stripper had ushered in my engineering employment career, a male stripper was now drawing down its curtains.

When I bade goodbye to the other employees in Albuquerque City Hall, I was surprised to feel a thickening at my throat. The drafting room employees had bought a cake that said "Good Luck" and fruit punch and coffee, of which everyone partook. I don't know if I felt sad over unchaining myself from a tight bondage that had tested and developed my inner strength, or over the misgivings of facing new uncertainties. Perhaps both, but again, they were sentiments overcome without much effort. I quickly retrieved from the files of my mind that, indeed, behind each option lurks new problems but a solution always exists, as sure as there is a ramp to every bridge.

Sipping iced fruit punch from a plastic cup, I ambled around, pressing the flesh, exchanging pleasantries. Goodbye time had come. After the last firm handshake from an engineer and the last tight hug from a draftswoman, I walked away from City Hall, my arms around a box of personal papers and a pot of plants. In very carefully measured steps, I headed to the parking lot. Once in my car, I drew down the window for one final unobstructed glance at the seven-floor concrete structure that was home for sixteen years. My heart was still heavy with conflicting emotions.

Then it was all over. My turbulent life as a salaried engineer was sliding into the past, fading like the clear view of Albuquerque downtown skyline as the tinted car window went up and shut. I took a deep breath and vowed to return someday not as an employee but as something else. Chairman of the Board. Head Honcho of my engineering consulting firm. Chief Executive Officer. Hot Shot. When I switched on the ignition key, my voice drowned the roar of the engine as I screamed like a maniac: "Yes sir! Call me Madame President! No less!"

In 1983, I founded Rhombus Professional Associates, Inc. with two thousand dollars, rented surveying equipment, and a laborer plucked from the state unemployment office. Started as a civil engineering and surveying company, it has since grown into a full-service engineering and environmental consulting firm that employs engineers, surveyors, scientists, and technicians. Against nearly insurmountable odds, my company, too, has attained a certain measure of success. But that will be another story, another time.

# Chapter 19

# The Spiel

I began the book by saying I'm different. I will end it by stating I'm not different from you.

A quarter of a century has passed since those tough pioneering days in engineering. Each year brought its fierce battles, but each year, too, brought joyous moments of victory sweet and intense enough to efface the nightmares in memory. The battle wound has long healed, mended by the soothing panacea of money, time and respect. The scar will always be there as a constant reminder that it had not been easy.

Not everybody is crazy about engineering. Not everybody would take a leisurely detour, while sightseeing in another city, to observe the design of a garbage dump. Not everybody would be inclined to drive out in a blinding rainstorm just to follow and analyze the flow of street flood. But everybody dreams. Everybody nurtures certain ambitions. A bridegroom dreams of a mortgage-free house for his family. A stage mother can hardly wait for the day a Broadway theater marquee flashes her daughter's name. A tennis player nurtures a vision of himself, on his knees, offering to the heavens his shiny round trophy at the center court of Wimbledon.

A dream could be as small as a housewife's wish for a new washing machine or as grand as a businessman's first million at age thirty-two. A dream need not be tangible. Dr. Martin Luther King, Jr. had a dream that one day his black brothers and sisters would enjoy the same civil rights as his white brothers and sisters. Mahatma Gandhi had a vision that his fatherland would be freed from foreign sovereignty through nonviolent resistance. One might dream of an audience with the Pope or a berth in an Olympic team.

## Celia Ruiz-Tomlinson

I like to think that my story is about a dream and success and the art of bridging the two.

What is this other word—success? The dictionary defines success firstly as outcome, secondly, as favorable result, then thirdly, the gaining of wealth, fame, etc.

The world, especially the United States, teems with rich, famous, or notorious people who are miserable failures. And yet, there are those who live on moderate means but are considered successful. Success, it seems to me, has two facets. The individual determines one facet and the people in his sphere determine the other. Marilyn Monroe might have considered herself a failure but her fans might think she was the greatest success ever, or vice versa. The same thing can be said about Howard Hughes. The encyclopedia bulges with names of other people who have achieved either fame or fortune, or both, but are considered failure by one and success by another.

I consider myself a success in the sense that I got what I ultimately wanted which is respect and recognition in the engineering profession. Whereas, some of the women to whom I have spoken at women's conferences rate me as a success for what I gave them. I delivered to them proof that a woman can crack any old-boy network, and proof that a woman can fight City Hall and win.

After taking stock of the present and summing up the past, I venture certain observations about the art of bridging dream and success, my philosophies on the art of making a dream come true:

**Differentiate between dream and fantasy.** Dream big or dream small, but be realistic. Learned or inborn abilities, the primary tools for the pursuit of dreams, set the limits. If the ability did not come with the genes at birth, and it cannot be learned through school or coaching, then the pursuit will be doomed from the start. We can work on dreams but we can only play out fantasies.

My biggest fantasy is becoming a vocalist. There is no end to my imagination about my dramatic entrance on stage, dutifully chased by the bright circle of spotlight, and heralded by the harmonious burst of the orchestra music. But I learned early in life that my vocal chord, having been designed for plain speaking and not for musical notes, has relegated my concerts to the confines of private rooms. I will never forget the mysterious silence that prevailed in the classroom after the first and only time I sang solo in our third grade music class. Thrice in my life I had been told unmercifully to keep my humming to myself. The moment of truth came home to me when I heard my own singing voice in a tape recorder in the privacy of a friend's backyard. I felt like crawling under the nearest rock. It was bad news, but it was the truth.

A dream and a fantasy are like a bird and the moon in the sky. A person can aim and shoot at both, but she can shoot down only the bird. The key to a viable dream then is honesty to self. Know the natural talents you possess and the abilities you can acquire effortlessly. Tailor the dreams around these assets.

**Selfishness is acceptable provided nobody gets hurt.** Look at all successful politicians, media personalities, professional athletes, and celebrities. All of them are products of selfishness. They spent most of their youth doing activities related to what they liked and wanted to be. They practiced, rehearsed, and studied crafts or trades they wanted to do. Show me a successful person and I'll show you a selfish individual. Read biographies of people who have reached the top. Notice something they have in common: ego strength, love of life, self-assurance, self-worth, and a sense of deserving more in life. These are non-palpable ideals that poise a man or a woman in a launch position. Productive, positive selfishness is acceptable because one day, after you've made it and reached your goal, you'll be in a position to think of and give back to others.

**Distance yourself from the crowd.** It's been said: You have to be different to stand out. Think of the famous rock stars. In their very competitive world, they spare nothing to look different. One painted black circles around her eyes, like a raccoon. Sinead O'Connor shaved her head. Michael Jackson wore one glove. Madonna wore funnel bra.

We remember the fastest in a marathon and forget all those who lumped in the pack. The bell curve catches a majority of the dots but the one point farthest away from the line catches attention.

Find your own niche.

**Take positive steps.** I raise a question: What would have happened if I had sat on my hands and conveniently blamed other people and circumstances around me? What would have happened if my parents had resigned themselves to the fact that we did not have the money to finance a college degree? It would be safe to assume that there would be no book to write, no heroic story to tell. We would have simply become a statistic in the company of people who resigned themselves to poverty. When my parents sold the family pig for my first tuition fee, they made their first positive move. I took my first positive step when I crossed the line that separated the engineering campus from the outside world. To have a chance in the lottery, one needs to buy a ticket. Tiger Woods began his rise to excellence when his father bought him his first golf club. Bill Clinton took the first step toward the presidency when he registered as a Democrat.

It makes sense. A series of short positive steps connect the bottom and top rungs of any ladder, including the proverbial ladder of success.

**Be prepared.** Can you imagine a soldier going to the battlefield without proper training?

**Be determined.** If I were to pick one single virtue needed to pursue success, it would have to be *determination*. Once you establish a resolute intention to accomplish something, you become obsessed. You automatically acquire a tunnel vision focused intensely on your goal. From then on, you undergo a transformation process beyond description. I will attempt to express it in a few words.

Enthusiasm envelops you. You ask yourself whether you want in or out. You become decisive. You recognize instantly that there is no such thing as half-in or half-out, half-enthusiastic, or half-decisive. You become systematic. Game plans leap out of your mind. You become patient. You persist in following Plan A. The killer instinct enters your being. Competitiveness possesses you. Aggressiveness rules you. Your hide toughens against blows of rejection and other adversities. You learn to roll your body into a ball to make the surface of attack as small as possible. Your head hardens and inside it is a rigidly disciplined mind but which is ready to flex if necessary. You put your emotions on a leash, under control at all time. You realize the importance of eloquent communication be it verbal, written, or physical. You become resourceful.

You know you must be present to win. You have to be around when your ship comes in. There is no such thing as an absentee success story.

You find yourself thinking big. You agonize for passing easy decisions in favor of hard ones, if they fit better in the overall plan. You condition your mind to let go of little defeats clearly to make room for the big win.

You maintain a reservoir of sense of humor because it is your therapy pool to keep your sanity. You seek humor to ease the resolution of doubts and the boosting of strength because you want to be in fine shape when you take on Plan B.

**Let go of the past.** Hanging on to the past, good or bad, can drag you down. Let it go. You can't change it. You can't go back. Move on and apply the lessons learned as you work toward a better future.

**Never underestimate people.** I had been subjected to so much underestimation and stereotyping that I do not wish such misfortune on anybody. From experience, I can safely speak against the evils of typecasting people.

When we were living in the ghetto in Manila, I remember an old, dirty, alcoholic bum that, during his binges, slept on the cold concrete floor in one corner of the market. Our neighbors talked about him as a worthless has-been boxer. They had no use for the poor fellow.

One day, following an altercation with Father, my brother Rodolfo, then eleven years old, ran away from home and left a farewell note saying he was going to an unknown faraway place so no one could find him. This sickened my parents with anguish. They asked the police for help, but to no avail. After two weeks of agony, something wonderful happened. The alcoholic bum went around the neighborhood, asking if any family was missing a young boy whom he had chanced upon while visiting his hometown several hundred miles away from Manila. To my family, the man became the most precious creature on earth the day Rodolfo came home

The man you belittle might be the person whose help you will need someday. The woman you underestimate might be an individual who is determined to prove you wrong. Think of what might have happened...

If I had written off my husband as a lost cause in the early years of our marriage.

If I had made a blanket judgement that all Americans were unreasonable and unfair.

If I had concluded that the men who crossed my professional path were all hopelessly inflexible and narrow-minded.

**Just go for it**. Anyone who wants to can cut a track between dream and success. Many people do. They set out to give it a try. Tragically, most of them buckle under early disappointing results and eventually allow themselves to get derailed from the path they have envisioned to follow. Sadder yet, some don't even make the first critical positive move because of fear of making a mistake. Others simply become impatient halfway through the project and quit.

It might have taken me more than twenty years to build my bridge between dream and success, but who's counting? Triumph is not measured by the calendar. Only the end result matters.

So hang on to the dream, but keep working and make it come true. ∎